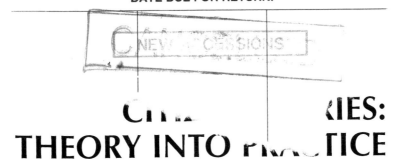

CITIZENS' JURIES:
THEORY INTO PRACTICE

Anna Coote and Jo Lenaghan

Acknowledgements

The authors wish to thank Deborah Mattinson, Viki Cooke, Robin Clarke and all at Opinion Leader Research who have worked with us to develop citizens' juries. We also thank Clare Delap, Elizabeth Kendall, Elizabeth Mitchell, Geoff Shepherd, Kimara Sharpe and Michael Evans for their hard work and enthusiasm, and John Stewart, Cheryl Brigham, Shirley McIver, Bec Hanley, Susan Elizabeth, Bill New, Peter Dienel, Ned Crosby, Kate Tillett and David St George for their encouragement.

The IPPR pilot juries would not have been possible without the generous support of Merck, Sharp & Dohme, Glaxo Wellcome, Pharmaceutical Partners, and the health authorities of Cambridge and Huntingdon, Kensington, Chelsea and Westminister and Walsall, as well as the Riverside Mental Health Trust. We are deeply grateful to them all for their faith in this project and their invaluable assistance.

The authors

Anna Coote is Deputy Director of the Institute for Public Policy Research, where she initiated and now directs the Institute's work on Health and Social Policy, Media and Communications, and Citizens' Juries. Her recent publications include *New Agenda for Health,* with DJ Hunter (IPPR, 1996), *Converging Communications*, with C Murroni and R Collins (IPPR 1996), and *Citizens' Juries*, with J Stewart and E Kendall (IPPR 1994).

Jo Lenaghan is a researcher in health policy at IPPR, where she has worked since January 1995. She was formerly a Clinical Audit Co-ordinator at King's College Hospital and a Research Officer for a charity for people suffering from asbestos-related diseases. She graduated in 1992 from Glasgow University. She is author of *Rationing and Rights in Health Care* (IPPR 1996) and editor of *Hard Choices in Health Care* (BMJ Books 1997).

CONTENTS

SUMMARY

In 1996, the Institute for Public Policy Research conducted a pilot series of five citizens' juries to test this new model of public involvement in decision-making. This report sets out the reasons for the experiment, describes and analyses the pilot series, and makes recommendations for the future.

- Why should we look for new ways to involve the public in decision-making?

- What are citizens' juries and how do they compare with other models of public involvement?

- How were the pilot juries conducted and what questions did they address?

- What did they tell us about jurors' attitudes to health policy, and to citizens' juries?

- What did we learn from the pilot series about citizens' juries and processes of public involvement?

- Where should we go from here?

Introduction

IPPR was the first organisation to carry out research into citizens' juries and to pioneer the idea in practice in the UK. The experiment was inspired by a critique of representative democracy and a desire to rebuild public confidence in the political process. A range of models are available for feeding the views of the public into a decision-making process. These include opinion polls and surveys, focus groups, referendums, public meetings, citizens' panels and forums, deliberative polls and citizens' juries. The usefulness of each model depends on how far it is appropriate to the task in hand. What are the requirements of the decision-makers? Why are the public being involved and in what capacity? "The public" have complex identities and different interests which may conflict – for example, as service users, as members of special interest groups, as neighbours and community members, voters and taxpayers.

What is a citizens' jury?

Citizens' juries involve the public in their capacity as ordinary citizens with no special axe to grind. They are usually commissioned by an organisation which has power to act on their recommendations. Between 12 and 16 jurors are recruited, using a combination of random and stratified sampling, to be broadly representative of their community. Their task is to address an important question about policy or planning. They are brought together for four days, with a team of two moderators. They are fully briefed about the background to the question, through written information and evidence from witnesses. Jurors scrutinise the information, cross examine the witnesses and discuss different aspects of the question in small groups and plenary sessions. Their conclusions are compiled in a report which is returned to the jurors for their approval before being submitted to the commissioning authority. The jury's verdict need not be unanimous, nor is it binding. However, the commissioning authority is required to publicise the jury and its findings, to respond within a set time and either to follow its recommendations or to explain publicly why not.

Compared with other models, citizens' juries offer a unique combination of *information, time, scrutiny, deliberation and independence.* Whether their findings carry authority depends on how far they are seen to be fairly recruited to represent the local population, and to be conducted openly and without bias or distortion.

The IPPR pilot series

The IPPR developed its model for citizens' juries in the UK on the basis of research into similar models in the United States and Germany. The IPPR pilot series consisted of five juries; all addressed health policy questions; four of the five were commissioned by health authorities and the fifth by IPPR. These were followed early in 1997 by a further three pilot juries, also commissioned by health authorities, sponsored by the King's Fund. A parallel series of six pilot juries commissioned by local authorities was sponsored by the Local Government Management Board. Both series were subject to independent evaluation by teams from Birmingham University. The report outlines the proceedings, decisions and impact of each jury in the IPPR series.

Jury One: on rationing health care
Should the public be involved in priority setting? What criteria should be applied to decisions? Should priorities be set at national or local level? Commissioned by Cambridge and Huntingdon Health Authority.

Juries Two and Three: on mental health services
What can be done to improve the quality of life for people with severe and enduring mental illness, carers and their neighbours? Commissioned by Kensington, Chelsea and Westminster Health Authority and the Riverside Mental Health Trust.

Jury Four: on services for the dying
What are the priorities for improving palliative care in Walsall? Commissioned by Walsall Health Authority.

Jury Five: on funding the NHS
How should citizens pay for health care in the future? Commissioned by IPPR and conducted in Luton.

Jurors' findings on health policy

No statistical significance is claimed for the findings of the pilot juries, but some strong themes emerged from the jurors' deliberations which are analysed in the report:

What kind of health service?
A large majority of jurors were clearly committed to the principle of equity of access, and strongly believed that all services should be free at the point of delivery. However, they want more information and choice, continuous and culturally responsive services, and better integrated and co-ordinated care.

Rationing
Most jurors accepted that resources are finite and were willing to participate in decisions about priority setting. Insofar as they had doubts, these stemmed from lack of knowledge about how the NHS currently works, suspicions that rationing means cuts, and a belief that decisions about individual cases should be left to doctors. When asked to set priorities, the jurors generated criteria that were similar to those used by the professionals but with different points of emphasis. For example, they stressed the need for a long-term view of the consequences, and the importance of local access, individual choice and high quality NHS staff.

Jurors opposed blanket exclusions from the NHS and favoured a national framework of guidelines for local decisions about rationing.

Public involvement

Jurors were generally cynical about whether public involvement exercises made any difference, but most thought they had a right to be involved in decisions, and felt a sense of "ownership" about the NHS. It seemed that involving the public and openly enlisting their help could rebuild trust in the NHS. It is not an awareness of rationing that reduces public confidence, but uncertainty about who is doing it, and according to what motives.

Jurors' views on the process

After each jury, the participants completed individual questionnaires about the process. These are analysed in the report. Almost without exception, the jurors were enthusiastic about their experience. They were glad of the chance to meet different people, to learn about the issue before them, to make a contribution to society, and to help resolve a policy problem. Nearly all said they would take part in another jury and recommend it to others. A substantial minority of jurors said they had changed their minds in the course of the session. Their criticisms centred on there being insufficient time to absorb information and strong doubts about the jury's capacity to influence the commissioning authority. Jurors generated a list of topics they considered suitable for citizens' juries, headed by education, and law and order.

Refining the citizens' jury process

This key section of the report sets out the lessons IPPR has learned from the pilot series about how to develop citizens' juries as a useful and credible way of involving the public in decision-making.

- *The commissioning body:* its motives for commissioning a jury, powers to act on the jury's findings and practical role in the proceedings; the importance of the jury's independence from the commissioning body.

- *Building a broad base:* working with stakeholders to prepare the jury agenda, to help ensure fair play and to encourage local involvement and support.

- *Recruitment of jurors:* alternative methods of recruitment; the case for paying jurors and for minimal exclusions.

- *Preparing for the jury:* choosing and wording the question; developing the agenda; documentation for jurors; selecting and briefing witnesses.

- *The deliberative process:* the role of the moderators; small group and plenary discussions; reaching conclusions.

- *The jurors' report:* style, content and purpose; jurors' approval and ownership of final report.

- *Public scrutiny:* policy towards observers and the media.

Lessons for democracy

The capacity of citizens

The pilot series strongly suggests that members of the public are willing to take part in decisions and are able to address complex policy questions. For this they require full but manageable information and the chance for reflective deliberation, for which skilful moderation is crucial. Jurors readily adopt a community perspective, thinking on behalf of others, not just themselves. The experience of serving on a jury appears to encourage active citizenship: many jurors expressed interest in staying involved after the session had ended.

The role of citizens' juries

The jury model appears to be more appropriate for choosing between clearly-defined options or for developing guidelines for decision-makers, than for producing detailed plans or considering abstract ideas. The momentum of the jury process tends towards consensus-building, encouraging better understanding between members of the public and decision-makers. A citizens' jury is likely to be more useful if applied to an issue where views have not yet become entrenched. Used appropriately, the jury model can help an organisation to resolve a dilemma, make wiser choices and to be more thoughtful and open in its decision-making.

Lessons for decision-makers

An authority considering a citizens' jury should be clear about what kind of question or issue it wants to address, what interests are at stake, whether it is free to act on a jury's recommendations and how much time and money it can spend on public involvement. It should be aware of other options and try to match purpose to method. Any public involvement exercise should include experts, interest groups, service users and citizens.

For the future
Objectives include: to refine the citizens' jury process, to develop and share appropriate skills, to promote and monitor further innovations, to build a network of interested organisations to exchange ideas and skills, and to identify and spread best practice. Interest in new ways of involving the public is high and rising. As innovations proceed, there will be questions about the integrity of new models, their effectiveness and their role in democracy. For juries to succeed, they must be credible and reliable. Poor practice could undermine confidence in them. Eventually, we may need to develop an agreed set of rules by which citizens' juries are conducted.

1. Introduction

This report describes a remarkable experiment in democratic practice. Between March and November 1996, the Institute for Public Policy Research conducted a series of five citizens' juries in a pilot project designed to test a new way of involving the public in decisions which affect their lives. These, together with a parallel series sponsored by the Local Government Management Board, were the first such juries to be conducted in the UK. We shall argue that the experiment has opened up new possibilities for democracy: it suggests that if we heed the lessons offered by the pilot juries, we might begin to transform what is now a rather sterile and immature relationship between citizens and policy-makers into something more dynamic and constructive for the next millennium.

Dysfunctional democracy

The citizens' jury experiment was inspired by a critique of representative democracy as practised in the UK and elsewhere. It is widely acknowledged that, although democracy is highly prized as an ideal, its implications for the modern world are problematic. In mass society, direct democracy is not a serious option. Instead, the people consent to elect representatives to govern on their behalf.[1] But what constitutes and sustains a consensual relationship between electors and elected? What makes for a flourishing or moribund relationship? And how much does the quality of the relationship matter?

These are substantial questions which can only be dealt with briefly here. In our view the main problems with the relationship at the centre of representative democracy can be summarised as follows:

Distance
In a large and complex society, the distances between the electorate and their elected representatives can be very great. The distance is perceived both horizontally (the geographical distance between localities and increasingly centralised government), and vertically (multiple layers of decision-making, reinforced by a culture of secrecy, through which information and consent must be filtered).

Distorted representations

The structures of representative democracy predate modern communications technologies. The two do not synchronise easily and adjustment is clumsy and painful. Citizens and their representatives must learn to understand each other (and themselves) as reflected in mirrors held up to them by the mass media. They cannot control the undulations of the glass, however subtle or sensational. Much grotesque posturing results. Can they find ways of looking directly at each other, or can they only hope to refine their skills of interpretation and manipulation?

Mistaken identity

Successive Conservative governments in the 1980s and 1990s have sought to redefine the citizen as customer. Political behaviour, which involves thinking and acting collectively to negotiate and change the conditions in which we live, is thus reduced to consumerism, which involves thinking and acting individually and passively, and which is contingent upon the individual's resources.[2] Accordingly, members of the public should be content to choose from products or services provided by others, and have no role in determining what these should be or how they should be delivered. The quasi-market relationship between customer and supplier of public services is real and important. But it is atomised and reactive, and only one part of the picture.[3] It can neither substitute for, nor be allowed to pre-empt, the political relationship between citizen and government.

No dialogue

Elected representatives in whom the public have vested responsibility to make decisions on their behalf, owe accountability to the public for those decisions. They render themselves accountable by standing for election every three to five years and, generally, this is where accountability begins and ends. But John Stewart[4] has argued persuasively that accountability is not guaranteed merely by democratic election; it is a two-way process. It involves *being held to account* and *giving an account*. This suggests that what is needed is, in effect, a continuing dialogue with the electorate in which the public has power to obtain and provide information, while the authority is open to scrutiny, listens and responds. If such a dialogue occurred, it would inform the authority's decision-making between elections as well as voters' choices at election time. It also helps the public to exercise control, informing its choices about conferring or withholding consent. Without dialogue, the relationship between elected representatives and the public remains superficial, stilted and predominantly silent.

Denial
If, as seems apparent, democracy is disabled by distance, distorted representations, mistaken identity and lack of dialogue, it is sustained by an assumption that citizenship is a passive, rather than active condition.[5] This assumption rests on a mutual denial of worth and ability. On one side, there is a widely-held view among decision-makers that ordinary members of the public lack the capacity to grasp complex issues or to form views of any relevance, that they are too gullible and will believe anything they read in the popular press, that their views are inevitably shaped by narrow and selfish concerns, and that they are generally apathetic and will not take the time or trouble to consider anything which does not affect them directly and personally.[6] It is thus futile or hazardous to attempt to involve them in any kind of dialogue. On the other side, there is a widely-held view among the voting (and non-voting) public that the decision-making process is hopelessly impermeable and whatever they do or say will make no difference. Many believe their own contribution would be worthless – a fear compounded by their lack of experience; most believe politicians are selectively deaf and unscrupulous in pursuing their own interests. In these ways, the assumption of passive citizenship serves to de-skill the people's democratic practice, justifies their continued exclusion and shores up their consent for a moribund relationship.

Bad government

Passive citizenship and an immature relationship between electors and elected make for bad government as well as dysfunctional democracy. Without dialogue in politics there can be no understanding. Without understanding, there can be no trust. Without trust, there is no real consent. Political influence flows through channels which ought to be peripheral rather than central to the working of democracy: favours exchanged, deals finessed, elite networks, spin-doctoring, the foibles of media folk.[7] What can ordinary people do? Nothing, for the most part. But then there are sudden eruptions of popular protest which seem to stand for much more than the issue immediately at stake. Whether it be a blockade against the export of live animals or the construction of a by-pass, a demonstration against hospital closures, or a riot against the poll tax, such expressions of active citizenship take on a symbolic quality, carrying a weight of feeling which cannot be distributed elsewhere. Opinions tend to polarise, views are encoded and differences over-simplified. Options for negotiation and compromise are closed off and the experience can be profoundly frustrating for all sides.[8]

Meanwhile, decision-makers operate with severely limited understanding. They may (or may not) consult experts and interest groups, read the pollsters' tea leaves, rifle through their post-bags, lunch with lobbyists, heed their pick of media commentators or simply contemplate their navels. They do not bring to the process any substantial knowledge of the views and experience of most ordinary citizens whose lives will be affected by their decisions. Furthermore, they have no obvious means of forging a compromise building a consensus where difficult choices have to be made between options where there are strong interests and arguments on either side. Government is thus deprived of a vital resource, often with dismal results. Homes are designed that residents can never cherish. Roads are built in the teeth of popular revolt. New but unloved shopping malls and parks fall to vandals. Health authorities save redundant hospitals to appease local campaigners. Two-thirds of voters stay away from local elections. Politicians sink lower and lower in the public's esteem. Distrust, frustration and mounting insecurity pollute the democratic environment.[9]

Our experiment with citizens' juries was born of a conviction that the situation is not hopeless. First, we must be clear about what is likely to nurture a flourishing, rather than moribund, relationship between citizens and decision-makers in a modern democracy. Then we must look for ways to make that come about.

Mutual trust and active citizenship

As we noted earlier, trust is the key. Not blind faith, but the kind of measured confidence that comes from informed understanding, forged in a mature, adult-to-adult relationship. If there were this kind of mutual trust, both sides could share responsibility for the difficult choices that have to be made in a "runaway world" – where the risks associated with new technologies and global communications cannot be predicted or controlled.[10] In place of secrecy, passivity and mutual contempt, there needs to be openness, interaction and mutual respect. Then the relationship could have a chance to flourish.

How can we begin to change the democratic environment? Stewart *et al* argued, in an earlier discussion of citizens' juries,[11] that the aim should be to build the "habit of active citizenship." Assumed passivity is the enemy of trust, offering no incentive to develop informed understanding on either side. But innovation should "work with the grain of how citizens actually behave" and acknowledge that "citizens are not the passive beings they are often assumed to be" – even if they never attend public meetings or demonstrations. They vote, if not in *sufficient*, often in *significant* numbers, not only in elections but in ballots on such issues as the opting out of schools and the transfer of housing estates. They do jury service – an obligation most take seriously. The process of responding to surveys could be seen as a form of participation, as could membership of a studio audience or a focus group used for research purposes. Innovations should build on such familiar forms to create a range of opportunities for active citizenship.

Citizens and service users

In considering ways of involving the public in decisions about services to the public, it is important to bear in mind that members of the public have a dual relationship with those responsible for commissioning and providing services. They are both service users and citizens. In each capacity they have different interests and these sometimes conflict. For example, in the National Health Service, individual patients have an immediate and personal interest in the service they receive. Citizens, meanwhile, have a broader and longer-term interest, as voters, taxpayers and members of the community: they are interested in what happens not only to themselves, but also to their families, neighbours and fellow citizens both now and in the future. These two perspectives must always be taken into account, but it must be acknowledged that they may conflict, for example, where an individual requires an expensive treatment which would use up substantial resources so that others could not receive the help they needed.

Too often, public involvement exercises confuse the patient/user and the citizen. Consulting the public is taken to mean consulting relevant user groups, so that individuals and groups who are not current users, but who may use the service in the future, or who do not use it although they need it, are excluded from the process.

Once the citizen/user dichotomy is recognised, efforts can be made to involve the public in both capacities. It is relatively straightforward to identify users and to locate them: they are usually in direct contact with providers, or organised in special interest groups for the purposes of campaigning or mutual aid. Furthermore, users are often highly motivated to take part in decisions. Efforts to involve them are sometimes insensitive, off-putting and futile: there is undoubtedly much room for improvement in many of the methods employed.[12] Nevertheless, it is relatively easy, if attention is paid to problems of language, literacy, mobility and small group dynamics, to establish a meaningful dialogue with service users – for example, by inviting them to meetings, by conducting surveys or by asking them to fill in questionnaires or comment on consultation documents. On the other hand, ordinary citizens who are not current users will either remain invisible, silent and excluded, or will turn, if provoked, to oppositional politics – where views become entrenched and negotiation futile. Different methods are required to draw them into the decision-making process.

Options for citizen involvement

A spectrum of possibilities exists for connecting the citizen to the decision-making process – from a simple transmission to a complex negotiation. Below, we set out briefly some examples to illustrate different points along the spectrum. How far different models encourage mutual trust and active citizenship depends on the extent to which views and information are exchanged, on the nature of that exchange, and on how power is distributed among the parties involved. Our list is not definitive and is merely intended to signal a range of generic approaches to public involvement.

Opinion polls can reach substantial numbers of individuals relatively cheaply and can be scientifically verified if the sample is large enough. But they are superficial and non-interactive, designed to elicit the *uninformed* views of the public through single or multiple choice questions. The organisation commissioning the poll controls the agenda and decides how to interpret and deploy the results.

Focus groups are a feature of qualitative research. They are usually conducted in sets, each group comprising 8-10 individuals recruited to represent a section of the population, and lasting for about 90 minutes, during which time one or more topics are discussed. While some information is provided, this is strictly limited and the purpose is to probe uninformed opinion in more depth than can be achieved by opinion polls. As with the latter, the organisation commissioning focus groups, controls the agenda and decides how to interpret and deploy the results.

Referendums can include entire populations, resembling an election, but inviting votes on a single question (for example, should the UK join the European Monetary Union?). Depending on the nature of the campaign leading up to the referendum, there may be opportunities for the spread of relevant information and for public debate, although this may be minimal and there is nothing built into the process to ensure that views are developed through deliberation. The media are likely to play a substantial role which may be more or less illuminating. Since a referendum must enable large numbers to register a view, the issue at stake has to be distilled into a simple yes/no vote and the model can therefore be likened to a blunt instrument rather than a precision tool. As a rule, power to determine what question should be put in a referendum remains with the government of the day, although in other countries there are arrangements for a people's referendum, where a sufficient number of signatures are collected in its favour. The results cannot easily be distorted or misrepresented to the public. If the referendum is binding, it confers considerable power on the voting public.[13]

Public meetings are the traditional means by which ordinary citizens are invited to participate in a decision-making process. Audiences are, of course, self-selected and in general, meetings are attended only by seasoned local activists or people with a special interest in the agenda. At best they can provide an opportunity for the exchange of information and views and for an open debate over 2-3 hours or longer. At worst, they are poorly attended, dominated by narrow interests and given over to the futile rehearsal of fixed positions. Power to set the agenda and act on the results remains with the commissioning organisation, but as the meetings are open and local media are often present, opportunities to (mis)interpret the event are restricted.

Citizens' forums or panels are gaining currency among local authorities and health authorities seeking ways of involving the public in their decisions. They come in several varieties. Broadly, they have a defined membership drawn from the local community and meet regularly for 90 minutes or more, to discuss a specified range of issues. Forums may be open to anyone living in a locality, or belonging to a particular range of interest groups. They have been used in some instances to negotiate a decision with the local authority.[14] Panels usually have a fixed membership, sometimes with a proportion replaced at intervals of one or more years. Members may be invited representatives of local organisations or ordinary citizens recruited to represent the local population. Because members meet over a period of time, they have a chance to become informed about the subjects they are asked to address, as well as to debate issues for a matter of hours. One danger is that panel members may develop an "insider's" mentality, becoming less detached from the interests of the organisers. The commissioning body controls the agenda and decides what to do with the results. Its freedom to manipulate the proceedings or interpret the outcome depends on the degree of openness with which the sessions are conducted.

Deliberative polls are a way of involving statistically significant numbers of ordinary citizens in an extended, informed discussion leading to a vote or series of votes. A national sample of voters is brought to a single site, for one or two days, to interact with witnesses and debate the issue at stake. Their views are polled, usually before and after the event. Deliberative polls were developed in the United States by James Fishkin and have been introduced to the UK in a series organised by Social and Community Planning Research, which was televised on Channel Four. John Stewart has commented that "deliberative opinion polls take as their starting point opinion polls and seek to correct their weaknesses."[15] The organisers control the agenda but the process is open and the results are not easily manipulated. Deliberative polls have not yet been commissioned in the UK by any official organisation but have been used by the mass media to explore public opinion in depth.

What is a "citizens' jury"?

The model described here is based on the IPPR pilot project, reported in the next chapter. Accordingly, a citizens' jury consists of between 12 and 16 individuals who are recruited to be broadly representative of their community. Their task is to answer questions on a matter of national or local importance.

What distinguishes a citizens' jury from other models? This particular process aims to combine *information, time, scrutiny, deliberation, independence and authority*. Most other forms of opinion research and public involvement have some of these features. What is distinctive is the package: the model is designed to ensure that all features are present to a substantial degree.

The jurors are brought together for about four days. They are asked to address one or more specific questions and are given as much relevant information as possible. They have the chance to cross examine the witnesses who present data and arguments to them, and to call for additional witnesses and information. They have time to deliberate – to discuss and debate the matter in hand, both with the witnesses and amongst themselves in small groups and in plenary sessions – before drawing conclusions. The jury is independent of the commissioning body and its verdict is expected to carry some authority, derived from an understanding that the jury is unbiased and the proceedings are fair and appropriate to the task of citizen participation.

Who convenes a citizens' jury?

Any organisation may convene a citizens' jury. In the UK in 1996, they were commissioned by a range of health and local authorities. Voluntary and private sector organisations, including the utilities and regulatory bodies, have also expressed interest. The juries in the IPPR pilot series were all commissioned by local health authorities with the exception of one which was commissioned directly by IPPR. All were asked to consider question/s relating to a policy or planning issue of some practical importance for the citizens represented by the jury.

How are jurors recruited?

The IPPR juries were recruited and moderated by the market research organisation, Opinion Leader Research. Different methods of recruitment were employed, but each case combined random selection with stratified sampling, to match a profile of the local population derived from census and other data. The jurors were ordinary citizens with no particular axe to grind. They were not self-selected, nor chosen because they had a special interest or expertise relating to the question before the jury. They were paid up to £200 for their time.

How are the jury sessions organised?

The agenda for each jury was drawn up by IPPR, which also took responsibility for inviting and briefing most of the witnesses, and for compiling the jury's report. For three of the five juries, an advisory group was set up to involve a range of local organisations in the preparatory stages. The jurors heard from up to four witnesses a day. The witness sessions and plenary discussions were moderated by a team of two from OLR with experience in facilitating group work. Each jury was expected to reach clear conclusions by the end of the fourth day.

What happens to the jury's verdict?

The juries were not obliged to deliver a unanimous verdict. In each case, the jury's conclusions, including minority views, were compiled in a report. Once this was approved by the jurors, it was presented to the commissioning body. The jury's conclusions were not binding, but the commissioning body was asked to meet certain conditions. It was expected to publicise the fact that the jury has been convened and the question/s it had been asked to consider, and to respond publicly to the jury's report within a set time. Where the jury made clear recommendations, the commissioning body was expected either to abide by the recommendations or to explain publicly why it did not intend to do so.

How much does a citizens' jury cost?

The total cost of a jury can be hard to calculate. It varies according to the amount of time required for the preparatory stages and how this time is accounted for, how much the jurors are paid, witnesses' expenses, and whether accommodation and catering are charged at commercial rates. We estimate that a four-day jury is likely to cost between £16,000 and £20,000.

How does a citizens' jury compare with other models?

Citizens' juries are closest to focus groups in form and to deliberative polls in purpose and procedure. They are more intensely interactive, providing more information and more time for scrutiny of evidence and deliberation than other models. They involve very small numbers and could make no claim to be statistically significant unless a series of juries were convened to consider the same question – this has not yet been attempted in the UK. Their status is independent, they can call their own witnesses and the jurors must approve the report of their conclusions before it is distributed. Whether or not their findings carry a weight of authority will depend on whether they are seen to be fairly recruited to represent the local population, and to be conducted openly and without bias or distortion. We return to these questions later in Chapter 5.

Table One below suggests how the different models rate in terms of the combination of features associated with the citizens' jury: information, time, scrutiny, deliberation, independence and authority. Table Two compares the models in terms of other practical considerations: how transparent are they, how many people can be involved, how much precision can they bring to decision-making, in terms of the detail and complexity they are able to tackle, and how much do they cost?

The tables suggest that the jury model has considerable strengths, and that its main weaknesses, compared with other models, are that its scope is very limited (though less so with multiple juries) and its cost is high. Other models have their own strengths and weaknesses and may be more or less useful than a citizens' jury, depending on the purpose for which they are required. Both tables convey the authors' subjective judgement: they are intended to invite debate rather than to present a definitive comparison.

Table 1.1

MODEL	Inform.	Time	Scrutiny	Deliber.	Indep.	Authority
Opinion poll	0	0	0	0	0	?
Focus group	1	2	1	1	0	?
Referendum	2	2	1	1	3	3
Public meeting	2	2	1	1	1	?
Citizens' panel/forum	2	2	2	2	1	?
Deliberative poll	2	2	2	2	1	?
Citizens' jury	3	3	3	3	2	?

Key

Information: are the participants informed about the background to the question?
Time: are the participants given time to consider the question before responding?
Scrutiny: do the participants have the opportunity to ask their own questions about the subject matter and receive answers before responding to the question?
Deliberation: do the participants have an opportunity to reflect on the information before them and discuss the matter with each other before responding?
Independence: do the participants have any control over how their response is interpreted and communicated to others?
Authority: do the participants' answers carry any authority?
0= no   1= a little/sometimes
2= some/usually   3= a lot/as a rule
?= not known/depends on other variables

Table 1.2

MODEL	Transparency	Scope	Precision	Cost
Opinion poll	1	3	0	2
Focus group	0	1	2	2
Referendum	3	3	0	3
Public meeting	3	1	1	1
Citizens' panel/forum	2	2	1	2
Deliberative poll	2	2	2	3
Citizens' jury	2	1	3	3

Key

Transparency: how far is the process visible and open to scrutiny by the general public?
Scope: how large or significant is the maximum sample?
Precision: how detailed and complex an issue can be considered?
Cost: is the model expensive compared with others & considering the numbers involved?
0= not at all/none   1= a little/a few
2= some/more than a little   3= a lot/very

The shape of this report

In the chapters that follow, we describe the background to the project and report briefly on each of the five citizens' juries, explaining where they took place and under whose auspices, what questions they were asked to address, how they tackled their allotted tasks, what conclusions they reached and with what effect. Next, we analyse the jurors' findings, both on the policy issues put before them and on their experience of the jury process. We then consider the practical implications: what can be done to maximise the integrity, credibility and usefulness of the citizens' jury process? In the final chapter we consider the political lessons to be learned from this experiment: what are the implications for politics, for national and local government, for other public sector bodies, and for private organisations with an interest in public affairs and community relations?

2. The IPPR pilot series

Preliminary research

In 1993 the Institute for Public Policy Research carried out research in the United States and Germany, where models had been developed to involve small groups of ordinary citizens in public policy decisions. Both innovations grew out of a critique of conventional democratic forms and a desire to free the decision-making process from the power of vested interests and a privileged elite of political insiders.

Germany
The German model, called planning cells or *plannungzelle*, was developed by Professor Peter Dienel at the University of Wuppertal, who began work on this project in 1969. Planning cells, which consist of 25 members, sub-divided into sub-groups of five, are commissioned by local and national government bodies, most often to address practical planning issues. Planning cells are recognised as a legitimate component of government decision-making. The model has also been used in Spain, the Netherlands and Palestine.

United States
The US model was developed by millionaire Ned Crosby who set up the Jefferson Centre, Minneapolis. US juries, which usually have 12 members, are intended to challenge conventional politicians and their decisions. Most are funded directly by the Jefferson Centre, but some have been sponsored by other organisations, usually independent of government; they have addressed a wide range of policy issues and use the media to publicise their findings.

IPPR's research findings were published in 1994, exciting a considerable degree of interest and enthusiasm.[16] In response, the Institute invited Professor Dienel to London to give a seminar, sponsored by the Anglo-German Foundation, for all those interested in the practical development of citizens' juries. Thereafter, the Local Government Management Board launched its initiative to sponsor a series of juries jointly with selected local authorities, while IPPR began negotiations with health authorities to find suitable partners for a parallel series. The first UK citizens' jury took place in March 1996, organised by IPPR with Opinion Leader Research and the Cambridge and Huntingdon Health Authority. This was shortly followed by the first LGMB local authority jury, organised by Opinion Leader Research for the London Borough of Lewisham.

The UK model draws on German and US experience but is not a replica of either. It is also informed by other UK experience, including deliberative polls, consensus conferences, citizens' panels and a range of television programmes based on citizen participation. It is being developed to suit the particular conditions and expectations of the UK.

IPPR decided to work with health authorities for two main reasons. First, there was already a strong interest among health authorities in developing new models for public involvement and consultation. Second, questions about rationing were high on the health policy agenda: as unelected bodies, health authorities were facing a crisis of legitimacy as they were obliged to take increasingly controversial decisions about setting priorities and allocating resources; such issues could not be tackled by clinicians and managers alone, but needed input from the wider public. The pilot series has produced findings on health policy issues, set out in Chapter Three, as well as insights into the processes of public involvement. The IPPR citizens' jury model has also been used by local authorities and would be appropriate for use by a range of other organisations.

The findings of each pilot jury were set out in a report, prepared by IPPR and submitted to the jurors for their approval. With the exception of Luton, each report, once approved by the jurors, was submitted to the commissioning health authority. Each authority undertook seriously to consider the jurors' recommendations and to respond in an open and honest manner. The decisions of the juries were not binding, but health authorities were required to give their reasons if they were unwilling or unable to implement the jurors' recommendations. Each health authority responded to the jurors' report slightly differently, according to the various organisational, cultural and time constraints within which it operated.

We set out below a brief account of the five IPPR juries which addressed health policy issues in 1996. The account is based on the jurors' reports. It includes the questions put to each jury, the proceedings, the jurors' decisions and a preliminary assessment of the impact made by each jury, based on the initial response of the commissioning authority. Further details about the juries' findings on aspects of health policy are in Chapter Three; details about the jury process are in Chapter Four and Five.

Jury 1: Cambridge and Huntingdon Health Authority

Questions
This jury was convened to address questions about rationing health care:

- Should the public be involved in making decisions about health care priorities?

- What criteria should be used to decide about health care decisions?

- Who should set priorities for health care and at what level?

Proceedings
The 16 jurors heard evidence from senior medical and management staff of the CHHA, including the Chief Executive Stephen Thornton and the Director of Public Health, Ron Zimmern. They also heard from patients with direct experience of clinical conditions under discussion, from health economist Frank Honigsbaum, from Philip Hunt, Director of NAHAT and from Professor Maurice Lessof, President of the Royal College of Physicians. They called two additional witnesses: a local fundholding GP, Dr Denis Cox, and Ron Abbott, chair of the Huntingdon Community Health Council.

Jurors deliberated in plenary sessions and smaller groups; they received written evidence, and completed questionnaires before and after the jury session. The plenary sessions and some of the smaller groups were moderated; men and women were separated for the smaller group discussions, as men tended to dominate the plenary sessions at first.

Decisions
- The public should be involved in decision-making; their views should be taken into account with those of professionals and other experts. When asked to say how important public involvement was on a scale of 1-10, the average score was 7.

- Jurors developed their own criteria for deciding about health care provision, listed in no particular order, these were: severity of disease, quality of life, effectiveness, can we afford it? how many will benefit? clinical judgement, views of the individual, need, progress, best for general public, fairness, local flexibility. They agreed that these were similar to the criteria adopted by the CHHA: equity, effectiveness, efficiency, appropriateness, accessibility, responsiveness.

• After considering a case study, jurors decided (some reluctantly) that quantity mattered more than quality. They had been asked to consider the relative merits of two types of pacemaker for those marginal cases (15 per cent of the total) where there was no clear clinical reason to prescribe one rather than the other. The simple pacemaker brought fewer benefits to the patient, but cost less and could therefore be given to larger numbers. The complex model had added advantages but cost more, which meant that fewer could enjoy it. The jurors voted by 12 to 4 that the simple pacemaker should be prescribed in the marginal cases.

• All but one decided that a priority (expressed as 60 per cent of a hypothetical budget) should be given to effective treatments for minor ailments, rather than to unproven treatments for major conditions. The case study they had been asked to consider was a simple operation, costing £600, to correct a deviated nasal septum, which had a 70 per cent effectiveness rate.

• All jurors agreed that there should be a national body set up to consider priority setting in the NHS. Thirteen agreed that it should issue broad and flexible guidelines; two that it should issue specific directives (one juror voted for both options). Asked who should sit on the national body, 16 voted for health economists and health managers, 15 for doctors and lay members of the public, 14 for patients' representatives, 8 for ethicists, 4 for social scientists and nil for politicians.

Impact

The Cambridge and Huntingdon Health Authority debated the report of the citizens' jury, and considered the value of the process within six weeks of the jury, at a public meeting of the full board. Jurors were invited to attend, but without speaking rights. The board of the Health Authority agreed that the jury had been a successful pilot which had potential as a method, and agreed to feed the findings of the jury into their long term purchasing strategy, alongside other consultation processes.

Jury 2 & 3: Kensington, Chelsea and Westminster Health Authority, and the Riverside Mental Health Trust

Two juries, one with 15 members, the other with 16 were held in May and June 1996 where they addressed similar questions about mental health services. The main question put to both was:

- What can be done to improve the quality of life for people with severe and enduring mental illness, carers and their neighbours?

The two juries heard from many of the same witnesses, although there were some variations. The wording of the questions and the agenda were refined after the first jury, to help achieve a clearer set of conclusions. Nevertheless, the fact that the two were conducted within weeks of one another provided a rare opportunity for comparison. The second KCW/Riverside jury was filmed by a team from Divers Productions who later produced a video of the proceedings.[17] We summarise the main points of the two juries below.

KCW/Riverside One

Question
In addition to the main question, the jury was asked:

- How can life be made better for users of mental health services and their neighbours?

- What factors should guide decisions locating people with severe and enduring mental illness?

Proceedings
Jurors heard evidence from mental health and other health experts, representatives of the health authority and mental health trust, users of mental health services, a social worker, a carer of a mentally ill person, a representative of MIND and a local resident. They also called their own witnesses: a clinical psychologist, a social worker specialising in outreach work with homeless people, and a black user of mental health services with his carer. The jurors received written evidence, filled in questionnaires before and after the session, and deliberated in moderated plenary sessions and in three unmoderated smaller groups (not single-sex).

Decisions
Asked about special accommodation, the jurors agreed that this was a good idea for certain categories. Individual projects should be evenly spread throughout a community, giving easy access to community facilities, shops, etc. Efforts should be made to integrate any future projects into normal/mixed socio-economic areas, neither wealthy nor poor, and not to locate them away from the community, for example on industrial estates. Local and health authorities should publicise their intentions about new

projects, informing all householders individually, and mounting public awareness campaigns. Residents should have the right to complain and the responsible authority should be accountable to local residents.

On the final day the jurors made the following general recommendations:

- All service providers need to liaise more closely

- Professionals need more support

- Communications between the different agencies need to be improved

- There should be more localised assessment

- More services for black people are required

- More money could be spent on
    a 24-hour Crisis Centre with a Users' Charter
    more homeless teams/workers
    more accommodation to be made available
    improved communication between agencies

- Less money could be spent on medication, with expenditure in this area to be investigated.

KCW/Riverside Two

Question
In addition to the main question, the jury was asked to consider what was good, bad and lacking in provision of services

- to people in special accommodation with 24-hour staffing

- to people living independently at home.

Proceedings
Jurors heard from the same range of witnesses as the previous jury, except for the witnesses they called themselves. This jury called one only: a representative of the National Schizophrenic Fellowship Carers' Forum. They received written evidence, filled in questionnaires before and after the session, and deliberated in moderated plenary sessions and in three unmoderated (mixed) smaller groups.

Decisions
The jury was asked on Day Four to prioritise its three most important recommendations for users, carers and the community.

● For users:
  more professional care and training
  community centres and a 24-hour crisis centre
  more home visits and aftercare linked with continuity of relationships and communications between services.

(Jurors also requested that attention be drawn to the need for gender appropriate accommodation.)

● For carers:
  one-stop service to include 24-hour drop-in and helpline, which would also serve as a way of bringing different professionals together.
  liaison between medical and social services, including better informed GPs
  more use made of up-to-date drugs, using them early in diagnosis and immediate help for users which might mean immediate access to a bed or admission to hospital.

(It was unanimously agreed by the jurors that there should be more help for users which would then help carers. This should involve more public money being allocated to mental health services, more education and the raising of public awareness on mental health.)

● For the community:
  someone to contact in an emergency with continuous up-date of information
  safety assurances and more education
  direct and honest consultation with the local community.

Impact of KCW/Riverside Juries One and Two
KCW Health Authority considered and debated the report of the citizens' jury as well as the process within three months of the two citizens' juries at a full meeting of the board. All members of the jurors were invited to attend not just the meeting, but to sit at the table and present their findings to the chair, Sir Thomas Boyd-Carpenter. The proceedings were filmed and open to the public. Sir Thomas Boyd-carpenter produced a written action plan responding to each of the jurors' recommendations, which generally

welcomed their findings, and agreed to produce a further report in six months time in order to ensure implementation. It was agreed that a response from the Riverside Mental Health Trust should be included in the implementation plan.

Jury 4: Walsall Health Authority

Question

- What are the priorities for improving palliative care in Walsall?

Palliative care is care for people who are terminally ill. The jury was asked to consider how an indicative figure of £600,000 could best be spent to improve services for people who were dying. During the four days, jurors were presented with four alternative models:

- Model 1: Palliative care at home

- Model 2: Inpatient hospice

- Model 3: Dedicated ward at the local Manor Hospital

- Model 4: A specialised nursing home.

Proceedings
The 16-strong jury heard evidence from management and medical staff at Walsall Health Authority; representatives of local support groups, the local campaign for an inpatient hospice, and the community health council; patients' relatives; hospice staff; social workers. Invited to call their own witnesses on Day Four, they called Peter Tebbit, a consultant from the National Council for Hospices and Palliative Care and the local MP, Bruce George; they also recalled Mike Marshall from the Sister Dora Hospice appeal and the Chief Executive of the health authority, Michael Evans. They considered each of the models in turn, received written evidence, filled in questionnaires before and after the session, and deliberated in moderated plenary sessions and unmoderated smaller (mixed) groups.

Decisions
The jury did not opt for one of the four models. Instead, jurors set out broad objectives for the health authority and then set priorities in terms of the short, medium and longer-term, taking account of the fact that resources were

limited. As an overall strategy, the jury recommended that the authority
should:

- Create a specialist palliative care unit in Walsall, based on the concept
  of a "hospice with a difference"

- Improve quality and amount of palliative and terminal care in the
  community, in order to enable more people to die at home if desired

- Improve the quality of palliative care provided at the Manor Hospital.

There was some disagreement among the jurors as to who should provide the
specialist palliative care unit. Broadly, the jury was supportive of the aims of
the Sister Dora Hospice Appeal, but were unconvinced that this charitable
organisation would have the capacity to raise the kind of money that would
be required. Thirteen jurors concluded that they would like the health
authority to explore further the feasibility of Model 4, based on the concept
of a "hospice with a difference", and to consider whether a private company
providing nursing homes could form a partnership with the voluntary sector
and the NHS in order to meet local needs in an affordable manner. Three
jurors remained convinced that a dedicated hospital ward was the best way to
improve services, but the other 13 decided that a hospital was an
inappropriate environment for people who were terminally ill.

Strategy for the short term:

- Palliative care in the community
      increase the amount of money available for palliative care
      increase nursing support so that there is a 24-hour easily
      contactable service, which may require more district nurses, Marie
      Curie and/or Macmillan nurses
      provide a full-time consultant in palliative care based in Walsall.

- Palliative care in the Manor hospital
      instigate an immediate review into the management of palliative
      care in the Manor hospital
      increase the amount of information available to patients and their
      carers concerning the availability of support and options for care

- Specialist palliative care unit
      Begin consultation and exploration on the possibility of providing
      a "hospice with a difference".

Strategy for the medium term:

- Improve quality of dying

- Increase the availability of respite care

- Increase the availability of bereavement counselling

- Gradually increase the numbers of specialist carers

- Introduce GP facilitators

- Encourage the continuing education of professionals

- Ensure that the service is flexible enough to adapt to future changes

- Buy more beds from existing hospices

- Improve communication between professionals

- Strive to improve continually the quality and amount of palliative care in Walsall.

Strategy for the longer term:

- Develop a specialist palliative care unit which should
    offer quality dying
    be staffed by specially trained and high-quality staff, providing a base for a full-time consultant in palliative care and Macmillan nurses
    offer day, respite and residential care, so that there is continuity of care for both patient and carer.

Impact

Walsall Health Authority considered the report of the citizens' jury as well as the process within one month of publication at a full board meeting, to which all jurors were invited. WHA provided a full written response to the recommendations of the jurors, undertaking to implement or explore most of their points. WHA has subsequently sent progress reports to the jurors and is committed to meeting them in June 1997 to discuss the development of the Palliative Care Programme.

Jury 5: Luton

The Luton jury was commissioned directly by IPPR, to establish the value of the citizens' jury model for dealing with issues of national concern. Although it took place with the knowledge and consent of the local health authority and the local Community Health Council, IPPR remained entirely responsible for setting the question, organising the proceedings and dealing with the results. Luton was chosen as a venue because it was a key marginal seat and as such was expected to offer a useful indication of the public's views in the period prior to the 1997 general election.

Question

● How should citizens pay for health services in the future?

The jury was asked to consider four distinctive but not mutually exclusive models: general taxation, hypothecated ("earmarked") tax, user charges and an increased role for private insurance. On the final day they were asked to address more detailed questions, listed below.

Proceedings

The 13 jurors heard from a total of seven witnesses, including two to explain the background and future prospects for NHS funding requirements, one advocate for each of the four models and (their own choice for the final day) the Chief Executive of Luton and Dunstable Hospital Trust, Bob Angel. They considered each of the models in turn, received written evidence, filled in questionnaires before and after the session, and deliberated in moderated plenary sessions and unmoderated smaller groups.

Decisions

What are the three most important qualities for a health service in the future?

● Top quality

● free-at-the-point-of-delivery

● equitable.

What should be the *main* method of funding health services?

● Unanimous support for NHS funds continuing to be collected via general taxation. A majority (10 for; 3 against) wanted "a certain amount safeguarded" specifically for the NHS.

What *additional* methods should be used to pay for which kind of health service?

● Unanimous support for continuing but not extending the current role of private insurance in supplementing NHS provision

● A majority (9 for; 4 against) agreed that user fees could be charged for non-essentials such as private rooms, television, different menu, hairdressers, "frilly duvet" and telephone.

● A majority (8 against; 5 for) opposed charging user fees for clinical treatments such as cosmetic surgery and tattoo removal.

How can we ensure public confidence in the National Health Service?

● Jurors agreed unanimously on the final day that they felt "broadly confident" about the NHS. Two thirds wanted more public involvement to help boost confidence.

Do you think the NHS needs more money?

● Yes (unanimous)

Would you personally be willing to pay more taxes to fund the NHS?

● Yes (12 for; 1 against)

Would you be prepared to pay into a private insurance scheme for your own health care?

● No (9 against; 4 for)

Would you be prepared to pay a fee for a private room in the NHS?

● No (9 against; 4 for)

Impact

IPPR commissioned this free-standing jury. Its findings on will contribute to policy debates on funding the NHS. More generally, the Luton jury has helped IPPR to assess how far citizens' juries can contribute to the process of decision-making on issues of national concern (see Chapter 5). The proceedings were filmed by *Newsnight* and broadcast on 10 January 1997.

3. Findings on health policy

Introduction

Despite important differences between the five pilot citizens' juries, some common themes emerged from the jurors' deliberations and findings. In this chapter, we look beyond the particular questions which were put to each jury, and consider the jurors' discussions and responses to key health policy issues.

A range of methods have been employed to collate and compare views and opinions. Questionnaires relating to both policy and process were given to each juror before and after each citizens' jury. The deliberations of the jurors were recorded, and the transcripts, along with the data from the questionnaires, provided the basis for five jurors' reports which were drafted by IPPR, and circulated to all jurors for their approval, before being submitted to the commissioning body. Below we draw out key themes from those reports. Full copies of each jury report are available from IPPR on request.

Small numbers were involved in each of the juries (between 12 and 16) and we do not claim any statistical significance for what follows. However, the discussions within the five citizens' juries reveal interesting similarities between the concerns and approaches of the members of the public who were involved. We have attempted to identify what kind of health service the jurors valued and have focused in particular on what the jurors said about rationing health services and about public involvement. As these issues were discussed directly by the Luton and CHHA juries, much of what follows necessarily draws upon these two pilots. The Walsall and KCW/Riverside juries are cited more often in Chapters Four and Five, where we discuss what the pilot citizens' juries indicated about the process itself.

1. What kind of health service?

The five pilot juries suggest that the public have strong and consistent views about the kind of health service that they want for themselves and their families. When asked what they thought were the best things about the NHS, the majority of jurors generally praised the fact that the NHS provides equal access to care, regardless of ability to pay:

The beauty of treating all people without charge.

(Luton juror)

It does not discriminate between age, nationality or wealth.

(Luton juror)

When asked to draw up a list of qualities which they thought a future health service should possess, the following list was generated by the Luton jurors:

- Free at the point of delivery

- Equity

- Openness

- Accountability

- Public involvement

- Quality

- Choice

- Ability to adapt to change

- Reliability

Although it proved difficult to rank each point in order of priority, there was a general consensus among the Luton jurors that the three most important qualities or criteria for a health service was that it should be: *Top quality, free at the point of delivery, and equitable.* The level of commitment to these principles was strong, and jurors were generally hostile to any proposals which they thought might undermine them. Only one juror differed from the majority in feeling that equity of access was important to the NHS:

I've worked from the day I left school ... if someone else who's been unemployed since the day they've left school and they need the operation, I think that I should have a right to have that operation before them.

(Luton juror)

The sentiment was not supported by any of the other jurors in Luton or elsewhere. In Cambridge, as a warm up exercise on the first day, jurors were asked to write down what they thought the NHS was there to do in an ideal world. The comments were similar to those expressed in Luton, suggesting a widely shared conviction that the NHS should be there for everyone when ever they needed it:

> *There should be total health care for whatever is required, so that people don't have to worry about anything.*

(CHHA juror)

> *What you want, as a citizen, is to be able to be certain that, when you want it, any surgery is going to be available.*

(CHHA juror)

In Walsall, jurors were asked to come up with criteria by which they could assess four models for palliative care. Following work in plenary sessions and small groups on the first day, the jurors produced this list:

- Choice of services for patients

- Information/ongoing communication

- Quality care for patient

- Quality care for carer (pre and post support and advice)

- Continuity of care

- 24-hour care

- Quality assurance

- Flexibility (ability to respond to changing needs)

- Local/accessibility

- Efficiency/cost effective

- Individual needs (eg cultural, disabilities etc.)

The criteria generated by the Walsall jurors highlights the perceived importance of choice, 24 hour care, and information, which was also evident in the KCW/Riverside juries:

There does not seem to be any back up for the family ... there is no recognition on any level for the work they are doing and there's a lack of information.
(KCW/Riverside juror)

What they need is 24 hour support – it's no good all the counsellors going home at 5pm if you have a crisis at midnight
(KCW/Riverside juror)

We feel that 24 hour availability of the service should be there, together with seven days a week. Quality of access for everyone, regardless of where they are situated.
(Walsall juror)

There should be information available to patients... there should be more choice given to patients so whereby they're already in a situation where they're feeling totally out of control, that they can choose and perhaps have more control over the way their illness is treated.
(Walsall juror)

The KCW/Riverside jurors expressed the view that the NHS at present was too mechanistic, and not sufficiently people centred:

If the concentration was on the person rather than on the system you might start getting somewhere. But it seems to me that your model of the system is dividing users into categories, fitting the type of system into the category of the user.
(KCW/Riverside juror)

Instead of people approaching their GPs, is there any one out there approaching people who look like they have a problem on the streets?
(KCW/Riverside juror)

The Walsall jurors also argued that the NHS needs to be more responsive towards cultural, as well as individual differences:

Accessibility ... covering things like people with foreign languages and stuff. It's not only wheel chair ramps and all that stuff it also covered the people who couldn't speak our language and that's what accessibility was.
(Walsall juror)

In KCW/Riverside, members of both juries were concerned about the failure of the NHS to respond to individual or cultural needs, particularly those of black people. In the first jury in particular, members felt that users from ethnic minorities were more likely to be diagnosed as being mentally ill, and less likely to receive alternative care, such as therapy rather than drugs. The KCW/Riverside jurors, as in Walsall, wanted professionals to improve their communications with each other, within and between departments, as well with as users and carers of the services. Many of the changes urged by both the KCW/Riverside juries focused upon changes in the way in which services are delivered and organised, rather than large increases in funds. This was also a feature of the Walsall jury:

> *I just wonder about the co-operation between the different departments, consultant doctor nurses, the special nurses ... it takes money doesn't it, but there are other things besides more money, there's experience ... co-operation is extremely important.*

> (Walsall juror)

Although all jurors expressed strong support for the traditional principles of the National Health Service, there appeared to be little public understanding or knowledge about how the NHS is currently organised or funded, on either a national or a local basis. In Luton, for example, it was apparent from the pre-jury questionnaires that most jurors believed that the NHS is funded from National Insurance Contributions, rather than from general taxation. Out of all the pilot juries, not one single juror had ever been consulted by their health authority about health provision in their area, and none had attended any public meetings by their local HA. In some areas, (such as Cambridge and Huntingdon), the majority of the jurors had heard of their local health authority, due to, for example, media coverage of the case of Child B. However, in most areas, the majority of jurors did not understand what the role or purpose of their health authority was, or how it fitted into the NHS.

Despite this lack of knowledge about the way things were organised, the majority of jurors expressed strong views and perceptions of the health service. In all of the juries, complaints about the amount of money being spent on administration costs in the NHS were common:

> *Administrators are well overpaid and there are too many of them.*

> (Luton juror)

> *We're talking a great deal about the actual medical work, but is there anybody looking at the administration, the alarming rate it's grown, at the alarming*

extra amount of funds that go into it ... is there any way this can be
streamlined in order to release more funds?

(CHHA juror)

If you took out half the administrators then you'd save plenty of money that
could be spent on looking after people.

(KCW/Riverside juror)

In KCW/Riverside, the majority of jurors confessed to knowing very little about mental illness, and even less about local or national policies for the mentally ill. However, there was still a general perception that care in the community was not working, and that London was full of ill people who had "slipped through the net"

In the last two years, and I think everyone around the table will agree, that
wherever you travel in central London you do see more and more mentally ill
people on the street.

(KCW/Riverside juror)

Yet many jurors often spoke of their own positive personal experiences:

My father-in-law is 94 and he's just had a by-pass. When they gave him the
by-pass I was amazed because I thought they'd just let him go quietly.

(Luton juror)

This difference between personal experience and perception appears to arise, at least in part, from images portrayed by the media. In the pre-jury questionnaire, most jurors indicated that they received the majority of their information concerning the NHS from the media. When a Luton juror claimed that there was a crisis in the NHS, one witness asked her whether she had any evidence for this assertion, to which she replied: "Well the media says so!" Many jurors, however, were aware of the role of the media, and sceptical about the information with which they provided. The majority of jurors, when asked, cited the media as their main source of information, but expressed doubt about the accuracy of the information which they received:

I only know what I read in the paper, and that's all sensationalised.

(KCW/Riverside juror)

When you read the papers it seems that the world is full of mad people stabbing people, and it probably isn't a fair representation of mental illness, but you can't help worrying.

(KCW/Riverside juror)

According to the papers that Child B was refused treatment purely because of the cost, but then again the papers might have been wrong.

(CHHA juror)

2. The gap between demand and supply

The jurors clearly wanted a top-quality health service for themselves and their families. This of course begs the question: *how do we pay for it?* Many jury members displayed a high degree of concern about the perceived crisis in the NHS, and fear for its long term future. When asked what concerned them most about the NHS, many Luton jurors responded:

That in the future we will no longer be able to afford it and cannot really rely on the NHS.

(Luton juror)

I'd really like to know and see for the future that there's still going to be free health care for everybody ... how is it going to be funded?

(Luton juror)

I think people are worried that if they don't take out any sort of private medical insurance at the moment then it will not be too long before they can't rely on the services providing health care.

(Luton juror)

In Luton the jurors (without prompting) asked almost every witness whether they thought that there really was a crisis in the health service. It was clear that this was a common perception, but that jurors doubted the sources of their information (the media). They had little faith that either of the main political parties would significantly improve the NHS, and there was a commonly held belief that it was inevitable that the UK "would go the way of America", and that more and more treatments would have to be paid for privately.

Throughout the juries, the problem of reconciling the gap between supply and demand in the NHS was considered. Options discussed included: raising/reforming taxation, an increased role for user fees, an increased role for the private sector, limiting the NHS to a core service and local and national guidelines for priority setting. Jurors' responses to each of these approaches to the funding dilemma are outlined briefly below. A full account of the jurors' recommendations can be found in the individual reports of the citizens' juries.[19]

Taxation

In a recent ICM poll, 92 per cent of respondents said they would be willing to pay an extra two pence in tax to fund the health service. However, polling evidence is often contradicted by voting behaviour. We therefore welcomed the opportunity to explore the issue in more depth with the Luton citizens' jury.

Cynicism about where taxpayers' money would be spent was evident. The majority of jurors said that they already paid enough taxes. If they were to be convinced to pay more, they suggested that they would need a demonstration firstly that current funds were being spent properly, secondly, that their taxes would go to the NHS, and thirdly, that the extra revenue would go on health care and not administration. The majority of Luton jurors argued that they were reluctant to pay more taxes without a "guarantee" to ensure that the money would be spent on the health service:

It does worry me that we don't have any say on what happens between the collection and the spending.

(Luton juror)

The Luton jurors generated the following list, which indicated what they thought were the strengths and weaknesses of the general taxation system:

Strengths

- Fair

- It is easy to collect

- Free at the point of delivery

- Reliable

- Offers choice

- Control over total expenditure

Weaknesses

- Politically led

- Short-termism

- Lack of public voice/involvement

- Confidence gap

On the final day, all the Luton jurors agreed that funding should be collected via general taxation. A majority (10) then recommended that an element of general taxation should be "safeguarded" for the NHS, with three voting against this policy.

> *We feel that at the moment there is no guarantee with the amount of money that is spent on the health service. If education badly needs it, then they can always pinch a bit from the health service. What we are saying is that health service is important enough to need an amount specified, set aside and guaranteed that it will be there.*
>
> (Luton juror)

> *We should be looking for new ways of gaining trust and respect (for politicians) rather than changing the taxation system.*
>
> (Luton juror)

Before the Luton jury, only eight people said that they would be willing to pay more taxes for the NHS. After the jury, this increased to 12 out of 13.

An increased role for the private sector

Many jurors initially appeared to be suspicious of the role of the private sector in health care. Some jurors often referred to media reports about the industry being expensive and unfair:

> *Watchdog had a case on about a private insurance company a couple of weeks ago about a patient who had to have an operation that cost £700 and because he hadn't read the small print that said it didn't cover that particular operation he could not receive the £700.*
>
> (Luton Juror)

However, most jurors agreed in principle that the private sector should be there to offer choice for those who wished to pay for it, and that it could help the NHS:

It helps the NHS also because they've got a wider market to buy their services from ... it offers everybody more choice, the NHS as well as individuals.

(Luton juror)

In Walsall, one of the options which the jurors were asked to consider was a dedicated nursing home for palliative care, which would be built by the private sector, and run in collaboration with the voluntary sector. The involvement of the private sector initially caused some concern:

We didn't like the nursing home thing at all because we felt that most people have paid all their lives for the services that the NHS provides, we've already paid that, so we feel that we shouldn't be asked to pay again for care.

(Walsall juror)

There was a story in the press about them masticating maggots in the nursing home and we just again said that we want quality of staff. We were wondering about this profit margin, and wondered whether we could build quality of staff into the contract?

(Walsall juror)

A minority on the jury, however, disagreed.

We don't see any problem with profits. If the company's making profits then it means it's doing a good job.

(Walsall juror)

We thought that the nursing home was great ... I mean all of a sudden you've got a company that will build a hospice, which we all agree we need, in Walsall, at no cost to the health authority or the council.

(Walsall juror)

Jurors were initially concerned that quality of staff and care would be sacrificed to the desire to make a profit, and that individual patients might be required to pay for their care. Despite these fears, at the end of the final day the majority of jurors (thirteen out of sixteen) agreed that this option should be explored further. Many jurors were reassured when they questioned a witness from the voluntary sector in Walsall, and got a positive response about the private sector option. The notion of immediacy, that this option could be enacted quickly, also seemed to increase the attractiveness of private sector involvement:

Everybody agreed that there is a need for a hospice or some other help in Walsall. If we don't want the nursing home, the impression I get is that we could be waiting for nearly five, six, seven years.

(Walsall juror)

However, the jury requested that if WHA pursued this model and put it out to tender, such a document should include the following specifications:

- A guarantee that the NHS, not the patient should pay for all of the palliative care, no matter how long it is needed.

- A guarantee that a highly trained and specialist palliative care team would be based at the nursing home.

- Implement proper monitoring and accountability mechanisms.

Not only were jurors committed to principles such as equity and the NHS being "free at the point of delivery", but when given the chance to influence health policy, they tried to preserve and strengthen these principles.

Luton jurors were asked what kind of health services, if any, they thought could be provided by the private sector. There was wide support for the status quo, including the provision of private beds. However, although they felt the private sector should offer *choice* over and above current NHS services, most jurors felt strongly that it should not be *necessary* to go private in order to receive clinical treatments.

We actually agreed, all of us, that if people are well off enough to pay for some services then they should be allowed to in a free society, but we were then quite clear that this should only be in addition to a comprehensive range of services such as there are now.

(Luton juror)

Most jurors in Luton seemed happy with the current role of the private sector long as it did not have an adverse effect on the NHS. There was little (if any) support for actually increasing the role of private health care provision in the UK.

I don't see why it [private health care sector] should be increased. As a group we couldn't see any benefits in increasing it. It could actually end up costing us more as a nation.

(Luton juror)

We wouldn't like to see the private sector being substituted for any of the services and anything they provide should be as well as what we now expect of the health service.

(Luton juror)

Jurors in Luton were asked whether they themselves would take out private health care insurance if they could afford it. Of those who said yes before the jury (eight), four people listed reasons linked to *consumerism*, such as the ability to choose the time and the place, to have a nicer room, with one person claiming that the NHS fails to give you what you want when you want it. Three others gave reasons related to issues of *security*, expressing fears that the NHS would not survive and claiming that if they had private insurance then they would feel more secure:

If I knew that the NHS was safe forever, then I would not need private health insurance.

(Luton juror)

After the Luton jury, slightly fewer jurors (six out of thirteen) said that if they could afford it then they would take out private insurance. This time, however, all their reasons for doing so were related to issues of consumerism:

To allow choice.

(Luton juror)

Quicker response to non-urgent needs. Better external environment.

(Luton juror)

An increased role for user fees

In Luton, jurors were asked to consider whether there should be a role for user fees in the NHS, after hearing evidence from a number of expert witnesses. This question provoked one of the liveliest debates and strongest divisions in the jury. Jurors **in favour** of a role for user fees in the NHS gave the following reasons:

● More choice for patients

- Raise extra revenue for NHS

- Increase staff interest in their job

- Reduce attractiveness of private sector

Jurors **against** the role of user fees in the NHS gave the following reasons:

- Not everyone can afford to pay, so it reduces choice

- Health care wouldn't be free at the point of delivery

- Reduces equity, creating a two-tier service

- Not reliable, as costs could fluctuate

- Wouldn't raise much money

- It would be a regressive step

- Put people off using health services

The following services which user fees could be levied against were suggested:

- Non-essential treatments

- Hotel services, such as choice of menu and private room

- Choice of surgeon/hospital

- Penalty fines for non-attendance

Most jurors were prepared to accept user fees for "extras" but hostile to their being charged for clinical services. Some were concerned that the introduction of user fees would gradually erode the principles of the NHS, or that it would lead to a "slippery slope". After a lengthy debate, jurors were asked to vote on whether they would like to see user fees charged for "hotel services" in the NHS in order to raise supplementary funds for the NHS. Nine voted in favour of this option, and four voted against. However, the number in favour was reduced to five, when asked if there should be some form of individual payment for treatments such as cosmetic surgery and tattoo removal. The majority of Luton jurors appeared willing to support a supplementary role for user fees, but were reluctant to support their application to clinical services, even where these were widely considered marginal to the NHS.

Criteria for rationing

The Cambridge jurors were asked what values they would use if they were the Chief Executive of a health authority and they had to "shop" for health care for the Cambridge and Huntingdon area. This provoked a lively debate about priority setting and rationing. There was a clear division between those who felt that rationing was "inevitable", as there would never be enough money, and those who refused to accept this:

> *In each case it should be a doctor's decision, and it is up to the authorities to supply the money. They've just got to find it.*
>
> (CHHA juror)

> *So long as you've got the facilities to save someone's life, you've always got the question of whether you're going to use those resources or not. As we go on generating better and better techniques we're always going to have the difficult problem of, now you can do it, do you it? Can you afford to do it? There's always going to be a problem.*
>
> (CHHA juror)

After some discussion and debate about core services and self inflicted illnesses (see below), the following criteria were suggested, in no order of importance:

- Severity of disease

- Quality of life

- Effectiveness

- Can we afford it

- How many will benefit

- Clinical judgement

- Views of the individual

- Need

- Progress

- Best for general public

- Fairness

- Local flexibility

The jury's list was similar in sentiment, if not language, to the criteria already adopted by the Health Authority. (Equity, effectiveness, efficiency, appropriateness, accessibility, responsiveness), although the jurors were not shown the CHHA's criteria until after they had generated their own. The key differences were that the jurors were more concerned with the need for "progress". It was no good, they argued, not performing treatments just because they were expensive or experimental, otherwise progress will never be made, and the treatments will never become cheaper:

> *If you want to progress, if you don't want to go backwards, then you've got to spend money on research, you can't afford to stand still.*

> (CHHA juror)

This tendency to think about policy in the long term was evident throughout all of the juries, as was the concern about cost. In Cambridge the jurors termed it "can we afford it", in Walsall they spoke of "cost-effectiveness", not just for the health authority, but for the individual concerned. The exception was Luton where, despite some prompting from the moderators, the jurors did not wish cost-effectiveness or value for money to be on their list of criteria. The prime reason appeared to be that "cost effectiveness" was seen as a code for low wages and poor quality.

The Walsall jurors accepted the financial constraints within which the health authority operated, and set their priorities in a sophisticated and thoughtful manner. They did not simply demand that a hospice should be built regardless of the cost:

> *If we are going to actually have some effect on palliative care for the terminally ill in the Borough of Walsall in the next few years it would be foolish of us to recommend a hospice if, quite realistically there is no realistic chance of a hospice being provided for, in terms of the buildings, by the charity because they've got no money available.*

> (Walsall juror)

The Walsall jurors were originally asked to set priorities by performing a "shopping exercise", indicating how they would spend £600,000. Although this was completed, the organisers and jurors felt it would be more useful to recommend an overall strategy or approach for palliative care in Walsall. The jurors then drew up a list of needs which a new specialist palliative care unit should satisfy before moving on to decide how such services could be provided. They accepted that they were defining an objective that would necessarily take some time to achieve. They therefore agreed to order their demands according to short, medium and long term priorities for the WHA to implement as part of its continuing strategy for improving palliative care in Walsall:

> We think that the health authority should be left in no uncertain terms that whereas we accept that this cannot happen tomorrow we do not want them to think that they can get away with it and that we will have forgotten about it two or three years down the road.
>
> (Walsall juror)

In Cambridge, jurors were presented with two case studies to enable them to think through in more concrete terms the issues of rationing and priority setting. They heard evidence from a cardiologist who explained that there were two types of pacemakers, simple and complex. Simple pacemakers are adequate for most patients, and cost £2,200, whereas complex pacemakers can improve the quality of life for some patients, but cost £4,400. The cardiologist explained that the decision as to which pacemaker to use would be a purely clinical judgement in 85 per cent of cases. However, in the remaining 15 per cent, there would be no clear clinical reason for choosing one or the other. The jurors were asked: in these 15 per cent of cases, should a patient be given the simple or the complex pacemaker? The majority of jurors felt that the ultimate choice should lie with the patient:

> It gets back to the idea of the patient being in control, and if they decide what they want, I think they should have that.
>
> (CHHA juror)

The jurors were evidently reluctant to address this question, which was essentially a choice between quality and quantity. Although their witness had gone to great pains to de-medicalise the problem, the jurors did their best to throw the ball back into the doctor's court. They remained concerned that nobody should be denied clinical treatment if they needed it:

A saving, I think would be perfectly all right if the simple [pacemaker] was adequate for the needs of that person, otherwise I think that could be waste. I'm against waste, but I am also against not giving people who need it a more complex one simply because the money isn't there.

(CHHA juror)

Jurors tried to draw a ring around clinical need and clinical treatments, to ensure that any policy changes did not impact upon this key principle of the NHS. Although user fees were never mentioned by any of the witnesses or organisers in Cambridge, one juror suggested that this approach might help to resolve the dilemma:

Have they considered offering the single pace maker immediately, but if they want to pay the difference themselves, then upgrade to the double? From a budgetary point of view you'd be able to treat more people.

(CHHA juror)

Other jurors pointed out that if the complex pacemaker allowed patients to lead an active life then they were more likely to be healthy and less likely to make calls on the health service in the future. Similarly, in this jury and others, jurors expressed concern at the long term effects of short term savings. When the Cambridge and Huntingdon jurors eventually took a decision, eleven out of sixteen voted for the simple pacemaker, and this increased to twelve on the last day.

I'd go for the simple one. It might mean more money can then go and save the life of somebody else ... if it's definitely clear that it's not going to make much difference.

(CHHA juror)

I'd go for the complex, because if you really have no idea, then it is better to go with the complex one, because their lives might be totally transformed.

(CHHA juror)

Core services

Both the Luton and Cambridge juries had lengthy discussions about whether it was possible or desirable to exclude "non-essential" or "non-life threatening" illness from NHS provision. In Cambridge, the issue of core services was raised on the very first morning, by the jurors themselves. The issue of rationing was perhaps dominant in jurors' minds, because of the recent publicity concerning the case of Child B. One juror expressed the following view, which turned out to be shared by a minority of fellow jurors:

> *There are certain things that are available on the NHS that I feel shouldn't be. Tattoos are available, cosmetic surgery, which is purely for vanity, nothing else ... there was a little girl that was refused £75,000 for cancer treatment, and yet all the tattoo merchants could have paid for that.*
>
> (CHHA juror)

> *Well if people are going to go mental over what sex they are, then tough, I'm not paying for them!*
>
> (CHHA juror)

When the Luton jurors were asked whether they thought that the NHS should restrict itself to "core services", this also provoked a lively debate:

> *There's no reason why the Secretary of State couldn't have a declared policy, inform the public that these things will not be dealt with by the National Health Service and if everybody knows it they'd have to accept it, it's just a condition of living.*
>
> (Luton juror)

> *It's not that simple ... what about tattoo removal and cosmetic surgery? Just because it's not important to us now, we can't say that it's not important for the whole of England ... where do you draw the line?*
>
> (Luton juror)

There was a disagreement in Cambridge and Luton between those who thought that all treatments should be provided on the NHS (the majority) and those who wanted to exclude certain "self-inflicted illnesses":

> *I don't think that you should go on spending billions on people who should stop smoking. It's getting them to stop that's important.*
>
> (CHHA juror)

> *You could take it to the extreme and say "well why did you walk down that path when it was icy and slip an break your leg? Surely that is self-inflicted?"*
>
> (Luton juror)

Some jurors in Cambridge argued that smokers already contributed taxes towards the NHS, and that this approach could be extended to sports injuries (which some supported). The majority were opposed to such penalties. In both the Luton and CHHA juries there was a vocal minority in favour of some form of core services, but the majority of jurors expressed the view that such a policy would be impossible to implement and unfair in practice:

> *Everyone has different values, opinions and morals and you'd never get this system to work because you could never ever be able to draw this line. What is acceptable? What is OK? What is medical? What isn't medical? You know, one thing you might find extremely trivial could be life threatening to someone else. I find it impossible to do that. You can't draw that line.*
>
> (Luton juror)

> *I think it is very hard to draw and fast rules. I think it's important that guidelines be issued, but that the medical staff at the sharp end have the flexibility to work within those guidelines from above... there are always extreme cases, but it is the inbetween ones which are the difficult ones.*
>
> (CHHA juror)

Jurors were sensitive about the practical difficulties associated with introducing a list of core services. This was true not only in CHHA, where they heard evidence to this effect, but also in Luton, where no such evidence was given, and jurors themselves raised the issue. At the outset of both juries, approximately two thirds were against core services or blanket exclusions, with a vocal third in favour. Following discussions with other jurors and evidence from other witnesses, the numbers in favour of core services decreased slightly.

Who should set priorities?

In Cambridge and Huntingdon, jurors were asked whether there should be a national set of criteria to guide priority setting in the NHS, following evidence from two witnesses arguing for and against a national body to set priorities in health care. The question the jurors were asked was: "Do you think that there should be a National Council for Priority Setting in the NHS?" There was a tension between those who thought that there should be some form of national policy in this area, and those (sometimes the same people) who were concerned about the need for local flexibility and individual discretion:

> *It seems to be fairly basic, that if you've got a finite resource, X amount of money allocated to whatever, then national criteria are essential. Obviously guidelines coming down to the local authorities, but with each thing having*

*a right of appeal. But unless you have national criteria, you'll never get a
balance for the finite resources.*

(CHHA juror)

*Different areas also have different health problems. If you were in Edinburgh,
you'd probably have to prioritise heart attacks more, and put more of your
money into cardio-care I would think.*

(CHHA juror)

When this question was put to the jury again on Day Four, using individual
questionnaires, sixteen answered yes, there should be a national body to set
guidelines for rationing in the NHS. There was some debate about whether
the body should issue directives or guidelines:

*You could say that nation-wide there is nowhere that will do cosmetic surgery
on the NHS.*

(CHHA juror)

*That's too specific, because it doesn't take into account the times that it is
appropriate*

(CHHA juror)

On the final day in Cambridge and Huntingdon, 13 jurors said that the role
of a national body should be to issue guidelines for priority setting, with two
arguing that it should be more specific and issue directives. One juror said
it should do both. Much of the support for the idea of national guidelines
was not motivated by a desire to limit or reduce the services provided by the
NHS, but to ensure greater equity and security within the NHS:

*I think the guidlines have got to protect the people who are wanting health care
on a national basis, and must guarantee what they want on a national basis,
because what we've got here is restrictions on what you can get. A national
basis should be to protect us and not to save them money.*

(CHHA juror)

*I've been subscribing to this system in the hope, or the belief that I would get
the service when I wanted it and when I needed it together with my pension
when I retire. Now over the years more and more things have been excluded
... I could, if I wanted to, be paying an extra contribution and going private
to get what I want, so I think that the public have a right to be assured that
they are getting what they are paying for.*

(CHHA juror)

Jurors were then asked to indicate who they thought should sit on such a national body, the results obtained are shown on the opposite page.

The ranking demonstrates the low esteem in which politicians are held, and surprisingly health managers score slightly higher than clinicians. The majority of jurors also wished to see the public playing a role in these decisions:

> We'd like to see lay people represented on the national body, maybe even just as a listening ear to see what they're up to.
>
> (CHHA juror)

Table 3.1 Who should sit on the National Council for priority setting

Politicians	0
Doctors	15
Health economists	16
Ethicists	8
Social Scientists	4
Patients' representatives	14
Health managers	16
Lay members	15
Other: Social services	3
GP	1
Councillors	1

3. Public involvement

How should the public be involved, and in what kind of decisions? Do the public wish to be involved? Can this really help to restore public accountability and trust, or is it just wishful thinking? These issues were put directly to the CHHA jury and were raised by the jurors themselves in the other pilots, particularly in Luton. The following section examines what jurors felt about public involvement in general. In Chapter four we detail what jurors thought about citizens' juries in particular.

Do the public want to be involved?

In Cambridge and Huntingdon, a whole day was spent discussing the issue of public involvement. Jurors were asked on the first day: "Should the public be involved in making decisions about health care provision?" Initially, some jurors were unsure about or hostile to the idea of public involvement:

> *I think that there should be professional people to make these decisions on my behalf. I don't see why I should have to influence it. They should know what they are doing.*

(CHHA juror)

This was a minority view, but several jurors were sceptical about the idea of public involvement, questioning whether it was just an exercise in public relations. One witness highlighted the difficulties involved in priority setting, and the limitations of most methods, such as QALYs. The jurors seemed surprised at how fallible "experts" were. In one witness session, a juror exclaimed:

> *So what you are saying is that there isn't one best way ... so we've got little chance then!*

(CHHA juror)

The witness replied: "You've got as good a chance as anyone ... so feel confident that you can go ahead and make some decisions". For jurors to develop confidence in their own capacity as decision makers, it clearly helped if they appreciated not only the limitations of the "experts" but also the absence of clear "right" or "wrong" answers in health care. In Luton, jurors were less hesitant about the role of citizens in rationing decisions:

> *I think the public should be involved at some point, (in rationing issues) like we're having this citizens' jury here to decide things. I think in some way that a formula of that kind may be able to help us reach the decision that we need to reach.*

(Luton juror)

Generally speaking, in all the juries there was a tension between those who wanted to see increased public involvement (the majority) and those who thought that decisions should be left to the experts (the minority):

We elect these people who really are quite expert, a lot of them, in their field, who do make measured decisions on the total budget don't they, and perhaps they're right – perhaps X billion is all we can afford at the moment in relation to other things.

(Luton juror)

Well I disagree with you ... why because they're politicians do they know any better than me or you, who know what the actual needs are locally ... If they are so clever, why don't they justify to the public why they spend X million on defence planes and so on?

(Luton juror)

Would ordinary people know enough? This is a big job.

(KCW/Riverside juror)

Well the public making decisions has got to be better than a load of councillors.

(KCW/Riverside juror)

Surely you should be asking people with terminal illnesses what they want – not us.

(Walsall juror)

I think it is good for the ordinary person to have a chance to express their views ... because palliative care affects all of us.

(Walsall juror)

Before the Cambridge jury, twelve out of sixteen jurors said that it was very important for the public to be involved in decisions about health care services in their area, and this rose to fifteen at the end of the four days. Fifteen jurors also agreed with the statement that: "People should be consulted about their opinions, which should be taken into account along with other interests". One juror agreed with the statement: "People should actually have the power to take the decisions themselves".

What can ordinary people contribute?

When the Cambridge jurors were asked what they thought ordinary people could bring to the decision making process, the following qualities were suggested:

● Common sense

● Emotional response

● Panoramic view of issues

● Unbiased view

Jurors also spoke of their "right" to be involved in the decision making process:

> *You have got to get some idea of the public opinion, because it is their resources that you are using.*
>
> (CHHA juror)

> *I think they should have permanent involvement. It is a national health service. We're not talking about BUPA here, we're talking about a health service which we all pay for... [I]f you've got a situation where you've got a group of non-elected people that run that service, then you have to consult the public.*
>
> (CHHA juror)

What kind of issues?

Although we set fairly basic questions about the importance of public involvement, CHHA jurors were sophisticated in distinguishing between different kinds of decision making processes, different sections of the public, and between informed and uninformed opinion and to what extent public opinion should influence the decision itself.

Several jurors pointed out that if they were to be involved in rationing decisions, then they would need a lot of information. The public, they argued, should have a say on rationing issues such as equity, accessibility and local needs, but technical questions, such as effectiveness, should be left to the appropriate professionals. In other words, the majority of jurors had a clear view of where their own competence and legitimacy lay:

> *The limit of public involvement should be opinion. They shouldn't be involved in the decision making. Those in authority should take the feedback from the public and take note of what public opinion is, but the decision must be made by people who know what they are talking about.*
>
> (CHHA juror)

It seems to me that the main job of health authorities is to define how restricted resources get allocated. Now my personal opinion is that is a political process... I do not think that it can be made without reference to the people who it affects. The health service users are not simply the daily users, they are tomorrow's patients, and they should have a significant input into the way health and health care resources are allocated.

(CHHA juror)

Jurors were also quick to point out potential obstacles to public involvement, such as apathy, or the fact that people only get involved in issues when something affects them directly, and rarely in their capacity as citizens:

It's not apathy... I mean, there's a police station down the road, but you're not interested until such time as you need it.

(CHHA juror)

Other jurors linked the lack of public involvement with the lack of public knowledge about the health service:

If the public are going to be involved then they must be made aware of what is going on in certain areas where there may be problems.

(Luton juror)

How should the public be involved?

There were discussions in Luton and Cambridge and Huntingdon about how the public could be more involved in decisions about the NHS. In Luton, some jurors felt that there was not enough public involvement at a high level, which is where they felt that important decisions were made. One juror had a detailed proposal for creating a national board, with elected regional representatives, similar to a citizens' jury. The representative would feed local views into the national body, and report national decisions back to the local level. There was some support for this idea, although others were concerned that such representatives would merely turn into politicians. There was also concern that regular public involvement exercises, to decide for instance, how much money to spend on the NHS, would be too costly. The Cambridge and Huntingdon jury was critical of CHHA's attempts to consult the public so far. Referring to a consultative document about their purchasing plans, a juror asked:

I just wondered where this was displayed? How many of the public were involved with it? Did anyone see it, or is this just something to pay lip service to the fact that the public have been consulted, but they didn't say anything?

(CHHA juror)

In Cambridge and Huntingdon, jurors were asked to consider what methods should be used to involve the public in the decision making process. Jurors suggested:

- Refined citizens' jury

- Patient participation groups

- Increased forms of communication

- Other existing methods, such as questionnaires

Concerns were expressed by the Cambridge and Huntingdon jurors about the money which was spent on public involvement. Although supportive of the principle, they said such exercises should not be paid for out of health authority budgets and that a national body should not only decide broad policy issues, but also organise active public participation at the local level of decision making.

Accountability and trust

The themes of accountability and trust were generated by the jurors themselves in all five of the pilot juries. Many jurors expressed concerns that they had little or no say in how much money was raised for the NHS or how it was spent; that politicians may be motivated by short termism and political gain, rather than the interests of the NHS, that health authorities were unelected bodies and that there was generally a "confidence gap" about how money was spent, due to a lack of transparency, accountability and public involvement:

There's a gap between how the money is collected and how it is spent, it's that middle bit that's so grey... If those people make those decisions, how do they make those decisions? It's such a grey area, we're unsure about whether we see it as a bad point because we're not actually involved at all.

(Luton juror)

Several jurors said they wanted to remove the politics from the NHS all together:

I think that it (the NHS) should be taken out of the political arena without doubt.

(Luton juror)

Paradoxically, there was also concern about the lack of accountability for rationing decisions in the Cambridge jury:

Where does the accountability reside? The trusts are effectively quangos, the minister won't take responsibility, so who will?

(CHHA juror)

If there isn't any public confidence, I would say that it's not in the actual health service, but in the politicians, so if you build up that trust between public and politicians rather than the public and the health service, then the confidence in the NHS will automatically go up.

(Luton juror)

To improve the confidence there has got to be a lot more public involvement at a higher level. There's an openness that the public needs to know about and be able to actually see these things happening, not just hearing them but actually being heard and actually seeing what they've said being done.

(Luton juror)

A similar point was also made by the two KCW/Riverside juries, who said that members of the public needed openness and information from the health authority when deciding to locate special accommodation units in residential areas. The KCW/Riverside jurors suggested that if the health authority is considering locating a special accommodation unit in a residential area, then they should publicise their intentions, inform all households individually, run public awareness campaigns, open evenings, and be honest and open in their consultation about what kind of mentally ill people would be moving into the area.

If you want to have community care then you have got to have the community with you. If you have the community against you then you are lost.

(KCW/Riverside juror)

Jurors were also concerned about accountability of GP fundholders. In Cambridge, the jury requested a local fundholder as a witness on the final day, where they asked him:

Who treads on you if things aren't going well funding wise. Who are you accountable to?

(CHHA juror)

They also requested evidence from a local Community Health Council Officer, in order to find out who they were and what they did. On hearing the officer's evidence, jurors were impressed by the "watchdog" role of the CHC, but were concerned about how they could be accountable to the public whom they were supposed to represent.

Perhaps not surprisingly, many jurors expressed distrust about the process in which they were engaged. They took some convincing that the citizens' jury was not just a public relations exercise, and that the local health authority really would listen to what they had to say:

Well I just think that they (health authorities) have all been told to consult the public and they've all got on with it. It's difficult to say that it isn't a PR exercise, I would take a lot of convincing that it wasn't.

(CHHA juror)

It is up to the health authority to prove that this is more than an a PR exercise by doing something about the problems which we have identified.

(KCW/Riverside juror)

Depends upon whether a care unit or something comes of the jury. If so, then yes I feel that it is more than a PR exercise and that I have contributed something.

(Walsall juror)

As one juror urged on his questionnaire:

Prove me wrong: Make our opinions heard and progress our suggestions please.

(CHHA juror)

Comment

During the five pilot juries, seventy five members of the public expressed a wide range of views and opinions, often contradicting themselves as well as each other. We have been unable to represent all of the many and fascinating discussions which took place, but have tried instead to give a fair and accurate flavour of the kind of opinions which were expressed in relation to a number of key policy issues. There is a danger in over-generalisation, but it is possible to distil some common themes from the discussions of the five juries:

What kind of health service

A large majority of jurors were clearly committed to the principles of equity of access, and strongly believed that all services should be free at the point of delivery. There was no evidence from any of the pilot juries of any weakening support for these principles which have traditionally shaped the NHS. However, the pilot juries also revealed a strong desire for "choice", which was expressed as a principle, even a right, of all citizens.

Linked to the idea of choice was a desire expressed by all of the juries for "24 hour" and culturally responsive services, more information for users and their carers, and better integrated and co-ordinated care. Although public support for the NHS appears as strong as ever, it seems that the public are no longer content to be grateful and passive recipients of care. Our juries indicate that citizens want a universal service that is free at the point of delivery, but one that offers information and choice. They want a service that is built around the needs of people, not professionals and institutions.

Rationing

The five pilot juries also indicated that the public are willing and able to be involved in decisions about priority setting and rationing. The majority of the jurors accepted that resources are finite and although most said that the NHS needed more money, they were willing to engage in discussions to ensure that money currently available was spent in the best possible way. However, jurors' responses often depended upon the information given and the kind of questions which were asked. Insofar as they had doubts about contributing to debates about rationing, these stemmed from jurors' lack of knowledge about how the NHS currently works, suspicions that rationing means cuts, and a belief that all decisions about health care provision should be left to doctors.

When asked to set priorities, there were surprisingly few significant differences between those generated by the jurors and those used by the professionals. The chief differences were in emphasis. For example, jurors consistently demonstrated their concern for the long term effects of any priority setting policies and showed a greater commitment than the professionals to local access and individual choice. Jurors consistently stressed that high quality NHS staff were an absolute priority and took the view that investment in professionals would benefit users and carers. They opposed wholesale exclusions of specific treatments from the NHS and favoured a national framework of guidelines for local decisions, with a national body to advise government on drawing up the guidelines.

Public involvement

Jurors were generally cynical about public involvement exercises, but the majority believed that they had a right to be involved in decisions about the provision of health care. Most jurors wanted their opinion to be taken into account with the views of other professionals, and clearly felt a sense of "ownership" about the National Health Service which they paid for.

It appears that citizens are willing and able to share the complexities involved in decisions about health care provision. Involving the public and openly enlisting their help, can eventually restore and indeed increase, public confidence in the health service. Our pilots indicate that it is not an awareness of rationing that reduces public confidence in the NHS, but uncertainty about who is doing it, and according to what motives. Without an open public debate, the public will assume that all rationing decisions are about cutting services rather than the fair distribution of finite resources.

4. Jurors' views on the process

The purpose of the five citizens' juries was to assess their value as a method of involving the public in decisions in the UK. To this end, the King's Fund commissioned an independent evaluation by a team from the Health Services Management Centre at Birmingham University. This also covered three further pilot juries sponsored by the King's Fund and commissioned by health authorities in Sunderland, East Sussex and Buckinghamshire. Independent evaluation is a vital part of the development of citizens' juries and other models of citizen participation.

As a contribution to the growing body of knowledge about citzens' juries we set out in this chapter the jurors' observations about the process in which they participated. In the following chapter we then discuss the problems and possibilities we have encountered as organisers of the pilot series, and set out our own views about how to improve the process.

After each citizens' jury, jurors were handed individual questionnaires which asked them to comment upon their experiences. Informal de-briefing sessions with the jurors provided further qualitative material. The purpose of the questionnaires and informal debriefings was primarily to ensure that IPPR and OLR learned from the pilots as we progressed, allowing us to amend the process accordingly.

At the end of IPPR's pilot series we were able to collate the responses of 59 jurors (that is, all of the jurors who participated in four of the juries).[18] During 1996, all those involved with citizens' juries were on a steep learning curve. This may help to explain why the volume of criticism was greatest during the first pilot and decreased as the series progressed. We have, however, tried to include a fair representation of all the views which were expressed during our pilots by the jurors who participated.

Jurors' expectations

During the five pilots, we employed two different recruitment methods (see p.72-3). Both produced satisfactory levels of interest and participation from those members of the public who were approached.

In the pre-jury questionnaire jurors were asked why they agreed to participate in the jury process. They were asked to score the following reasons, when 5 meant that this was the most important consideration and 0 meant that they didn't consider this at all:

I was interested in	Average score
The idea of public involvement	4.1
Taking part in new piece of research	4
I was curious	3.3
The money	2.3
The publicity	1.2

The majority of jurors agreed to take part because they were interested in taking part in a new method of public involvement. Each juror was paid £200 for their time, but many respondents claimed that this was of little importance. From qualitative discussions, it appeared that the fee acted as a greater incentive for younger people and jurors from low income groups.

Many jurors found the experience very different from their early expectations. Some were initially overwhelmed by the amount of information which they were presented with:

> *Well, when I first got the invitation, I personally thought great, I've got four days off work and £200, but it's so intensive!*
>
> (Luton juror)

> *How are we going to sleep tonight, with all this information?*
>
> (KCW juror)

Some jurors evidently agreed to take part only for the money, but most said they were pleasantly surprised, and appeared to feel generally positive about their experiences.

> *It's been enormously interesting – I wouldn't have missed it for the world!*
>
> (CHHA juror)

> *I feel that a citizens' jury is the way to bridge the gap between them and us. I do hope it is the way forward, and that after this pilot it is not dismissed.*
>
> (CHHA juror)

It was a learning experience for me, especially as I was the youngest and most inexperienced member of the jury.

(Luton juror)

It was a great chance for discussion. I believe 100 per cent in this.

(Walsall juror)

I feel privileged to have been given a chance to be involved in this important issue.

(Walsall juror)

In general, the overwhelming majority of participants found the citizens' jury a positive experience. They said they would repeat it themselves and recommend it to others.

What was the best thing about citizens' juries?

Jurors were asked to describe in their own words what they thought was the best thing about citizens' juries. They were not asked to choose from specific options, yet their responses were remarkably similar. In general, jurors tended to praise the fact that the juries enabled them to meet new people from different backgrounds and perspectives, to learn about a new topic, to participate in decision making, and to foster a sense of community:

It has been an inspiration to see how different people of different age groups and backgrounds can work together for a common cause.

(CHHA juror)

It allows lay persons to understand the process of decision making in government. Also it helps us to understand topical issues.

(Luton juror)

The community feeling and awareness it gives one.

(KCW juror)

The chance to be involved in decisions.

(Walsall juror)

One of the important things that I found with this process is that each one of us had very, very different ideas on the NHS and as the 4 days have gone on, listening to the witnesses and everything else we came to a unanimous conclusion on one thing so despite the diversity of opinion it seemed that you can actually have a unanimous agreement on some of the very core issues about the NHS or any other problem.

(Luton juror)

What was the worst thing about citizens' juries?

Many jurors said that aspects of the process needed improvement, particularly in the earlier pilots. Here too there were similarities between the comments made by different jurors. Several said they had insufficient time to cross-examine witnesses, to discuss the questions amongst themselves and to reach final conclusions. The organisers gradually amended the timetable to accommodate these points (see Chapter 5).

There were some complaints about the amount of hard work which was required of the jurors, and the tendency of certain personalities to dominate the proceedings. Many jurors expressed cynicism about the outcome. Positive remarks were often qualified to the effect that their final judgement would depend upon whether or not the authorities listened and took note of their recommendations:

Time limits, but perhaps we have tried to do too much in the time allowed.

(CHHA juror)

Could be considered another toothless group.

(CHHA juror)

It is very hard work.

(Luton juror)

Easy for "leader" type people to manipulate passive person's view points.

(Luton juror)

Wondering if we have really made a difference and if we will be listened to.

(KCW juror)

In a short space of time we had to cover so much. I personally found it very draining at times.

(KCW juror)

Lots of information delivered too quickly.

(Walsall juror)

Only having 16 people to represent the people of Walsall.

(Walsall juror)"

General assessment: did jurors agree or disagree with the following statements?

Jurors were asked to score from 1 to 10, when 1 = "don't agree at all" and 10 = "strongly agree". The following scores represent an average of all responses.

I found the jury interesting	9
I found the jury informative	9
I found the jury enjoyable	8
I found the jury boring	1
I found the jury confusing	2
I found the jury depressing	2
I felt the jury put me in a position of influence	5

If asked, would jurors take part in another citizens' jury?

Yes	97%
No	3%

Would jurors recommend taking part in a citizens' jury to other people?

Yes	95%
No	5%

Is a citizens' jury is a good way of involving the public in decision making?

Yes	92%
No	5%
Depends	3%

What aspects of the process helped jurors to decide?

Jurors were asked to score specific aspects of the process, when 1 = "not at all helpful" and 10 = "extremely helpful". The following scores represent an average of all responses:

Hearing from witnesses	9
The Q & A sessions	8
The full jury discussions	8
The small group discussions	7
Informal chats at break time	6
Just thinking by yourself	5
Talking to others outside the jury	4

How much information could the jurors handle?

Initially jurors were given as little written information as possible, in order to avoid discrepancies between those who were used to dealing with documentation and those who were not. However, it became clear during the first pilot that jurors wanted and needed more information. They requested copies of the annual purchasing plans, a graph which explained the structure of the health service, and copies of each witness's presentation. They also requested time to prepare questions amongst themselves before hearing from the witnesses:

> *Some background information in advance would have been helpful.*
> (CHHA juror)

> *I would have liked handouts as each subject was discussed.*
> (CHHA juror)

> *More time with the witnesses – perhaps make the jury 5 or 6 days instead of 4.*
> (Walsall juror)

> *An agenda and proper briefing would have been useful.*
> (KCW/Riverside juror)

Did jurors feel that the information they received was sufficient?

Too much   7%

About right   54%

Not enough   39%

Fifteen out of the 16 CHHA jurors said that the information they received was "not enough". Contrary to our initial expectations, jurors appeared to want more, not less information. This was confirmed by jurors in Walsall and Luton: despite been given large amounts of written information, in the form of briefing papers and handouts from witnesses, hardly any complained that this was too much. But information must be presented in a concise and accessible manner (p.79).

What did jurors feel about the information presented to them in the course of the proceedings?

All of it went over my head   0

Some of it went over my head   12%

I understood most of it   44%

I understood all of it   44%

Did jurors feel they understood more as the session progressed?

Yes   97%

No   3%

Was the agenda satisfactory?

In each jury, we allowed a break of two or three days during the proceedings. In most juries, this appeared to be welcome:

> *I think it would be just too much to have it straight through.*
>
> (Walsall juror)

It was just about right as it was

(Luton juror)

The majority of the jurors found the length of the jury process and the two or three day break "about right", although three said that the break was unnecessary, and two said that it was too long. The break also allowed the agenda to be spread out over a combination of week days and the week end. In Luton, the jury ran on a Saturday, Monday, Tuesday and Wednesday, which appeared satisfactory to the jurors.

What did jurors gain from the experience?

The concept of citizens' juries is aimed not just at ensuring that more competent and legitimate decisions are taken by public bodies, but at creating a habit of active citizenship, and fostering a sense of community. What did jurors say they had (or had not) gained from participating? Here, too, the question was open ended, but many respondents expressed similar sentiments. Jurors said they had gained greater knowledge about the issue put before them, a sense of achievement, a greater empathy for their local community and personal confidence and satisfaction:

General enlightenment about the NHS and the difficulties involved in decision making, hearing opinions other than my own.

(CHHA juror)

Even if it turns out to be a "paper exercise" it is nice to know that people can discuss sensibly and non-emotionally issues which affect them in their own community.

(CHHA juror)

I feel more confident about expressing myself in front of other people.

(Luton juror)

A point of view.

(Luton juror)

More compassion for users.

(KCW juror)

I have lost a feeling of frustration and impotence and feel a sense of satisfaction at being able to take part.

(KCW/Riverside juror)

A greater knowledge of KCW and a feeling of responsibility towards the mental health community and £200.

(KCW/Riverside juror)

An education in the sensitive issue of palliative care. I also feel very privileged to have been given the chance to participate.

(Walsall juror)

A sense of collaboration amongst the people of Walsall "as a jury".

(Walsall juror)

More empathy with family and neighbours.

(Walsall juror)

Do jurors feel that they have contributed anything to their community?

Yes   70%

No   20%

Depends   10%

(This question was not put to the Luton jurors, because this was intended to address a "national" issue and was not commissioned by a locally based authority.) A high proportion of the "yes" vote was followed by the qualification, that it depends upon whether the authority listens and follows their recommendations:

No. I think that it is unlikely that our discussions will have any effect.

(CHHA juror)

I have contributed something I'm not sure how to explain it – I guess taking some responsibility for the community.

(CHHA juror)

Not sure – this depends upon how much notice our report gets and if any action is taken as a result.

(KCW/Riverside juror)

By offering my opinions and thoughts on the subject I am contributing my energy and care to the local community.

(KCW/Riverside juror)

I have gained useful education, but I do not feel that I have contributed anything.

(KCW/Riverside juror)

If a Specialist Palliative Care Unit is set up then yes, I will feel that I have achieved something.

(Walsall juror)

Yes, just by getting involved.

(Walsall juror)

Did jurors change their mind as a result of the jury?

A citizens' jury typically sits for four days, during which time jurors hear from a wide range of views from both witnesses and fellow jurors. Twenty-three admitted to changing their minds, compared to 36 who denied doing so.

The greatest change has been my attitude towards the mentally ill. I had believed they were being turned out of institutions in order to save money ... I now know better.

(KCW/Riverside juror)

I think I have been insensitive to the plight of mental sickness. I have wanted to walk away, but now I do have a slight knowledge and better understanding.

(KCW/Riverside juror)

On day 3 I agreed about the hotel charges, but when I heard all the arguments against it I changed my mind. I thought that I might as well go private.

(Luton juror)

What should be the status of the citizens' jury?

We asked each juror, (apart from Luton, where this question was omitted, due to the absence of health authority involvement) whether the jury's recommendations should be binding on the health authority. A small majority of 24 responded yes, compared to 22 who responded no. IPPR and others have argued, conversely, that juries' findings should only be part of the decision making process. The jurors' views may indicate the extent of their cynicism about the extent to which public involvement exercises can make a difference.

Should citizens' juries be open to the public?

IPPR has always invited members of the relevant stakeholder groups (Community Health Councils, health authorities, user groups, etc.) and the members of the local and national media to observe the proceedings. But none of the pilot juries was open to the public: anyone wanting to observe had to secure an invitation and agree to come at a certain time, with a rosta operating so that not everyone can at once. These arrangements depended partly on practical restrictions of space and partly on fears that anything more than a handful of discreet observers would inhibit the jurors' deliberations. Asked whether the proceedings should be open to the public during qualitative discussions, a small majority said no, but there was a clear division of opinion:

> *Yes, so that people can judge for themselves whether it is worth it.*
>
> (CHHA juror)

> *No, specific interest groups might be able to steer the decisions/ thoughts of the jury in a particular direction.*
>
> (CHHA juror)

> *(No) Restricts expression of creative thought.*
>
> (KCW/Riverside juror)

> *(Yes) To give the public insight and understanding and hopefully reassurance that they are getting their voice heard.*
>
> (Walsall juror)

What kind of issues do jurors think a citizens' jury might be most suited to consider?

Questionnaires and group discussions generated the following list, with education the most popular, followed closely with law and order:

- Education

- Law and order

- Drugs

- Social/Community care

- Death penalty

- Youth services

- Local planning issues

- Transport local/national

- Housing

- Censorship

- Europe

- Any situations which affect the public in general.

5. Refining the jury process

In the next section we offer some preliminary observations based upon the experience of the IPPR organisers working on five pilot juries.[20]

The commissioning body

Four of the IPPR pilot citizens' juries were commissioned by a health authority. Any organisation can hold a jury, but it helps if it has the power to act on the jurors' recommendations. The jury's findings in our pilots were advisory, not binding. However, the value of the process depends on how seriously it is seen to be taken by the commissioning body. Is it just an public relations exercise or an elaborate effort to "educate" the public? If so, why should anyone bother to take part or take note of what the jurors have to say? What is the point of spending all that money? To signal clearly that a citizens' jury is an honest attempt to involve the public in the commissioning authority's decision-making process, we recommend that it should make a prior commitment to:

● publicise the fact that a jury has been convened and the questions which it has been asked to address

● publish the jury's conclusions

● undertake to respond publicly within a set time

● where the jury makes clear recommendations, either act upon them or explain publicly why not

It is important to make this commitment before the jury takes place in order to avoid confusion and misunderstandings. It may help to draft an informal "contract" between the organisers and the commissioning body, to clarify the roles and responsibilities of each party. This clarifies for the participants the status of the citizens' jury and its final report.

As we noted in Chapter One each authority involved in our pilots responded in a slightly different way, depending upon its particular cultural and organisational context. Our final jury in Luton did not involve a health authority and instead was commissioned by IPPR and organised jointly by IPPR and OLR. Our purpose was to assess whether juries could be used to decide issues of national importance, along the lines of the US model. The process itself appeared successful, in that the jury handled the question competently and came to clear conclusions, but IPPR was not in a position to implement its recommendations. We explained to the jurors that they were participating in a pilot and that, as a research institute, the IPPR could only publicise the jury's findings and bring them to the attention of key decision makers. This appeared to satisfy the jurors. The fact that it was filmed by *Newsnight* probably helped.

The experience of the United States and Germany is salutary.[21] Citizens' juries in the US are run by the Jefferson Centre in Minneapolis and are not usually commissioned by a decision-making body. They have made little impact on the decisions of government bodies, although they have drawn attention to key issues through the media. By contrast, in Germany, *plannungzelle* are regarded as integral to the decision-making process and usually commissioned by local authorities or other bodies who have power to implement their recommendations. The latter approach appears to have more impact and influence and is closest to the model being developed in the UK.

In four of our pilots, the juries were organised and run independently of the commissioning authority (by IPPR and OLR). This has helped to reduce the risk of a jury being seen as unduly influenced by vested interests. Some authorities may prefer in future to run citizens' juries themselves. Either way – and especially in the latter case – care must be taken to avoid actual or perceived bias.

If the findings of the jury are to have any credibility or legitimacy, then the process must be seen to be unaffected by the interests of the commissioning body. As a minimum, we recommend that the jurors are recruited by an independent organisation, moderated by independent professionals and that an advisory group of all the stakeholders be convened to help develop the agenda for the jury and select witnesses.

Appointing a key worker
To be successful, a citizens' jury requires a firm commitment and a substantial input of time by the commissioning body. Even if recruitment and organisation are contracted out to other organisations, there are functions that only be carried out by someone on the inside. We have

concluded that the key worker from the commissioning body needs to be at a high enough level to ensure that things get done, yet not so senior that they are too busy to be involved. This balance may best be achieved by obtaining the active interest and support of the Chief Executive or Chair (or equivalent), who then nominates a senior officer to manage the project on a day-to-day basis. In our pilots, it has been this officer's responsibility to:

● convene the steering group

● assist with the recruitment of witnesses

● keep colleagues informed and comfortable about the jury process

● arrange house-keeping details

● be present during the entire jury and be prepared to supply extra information if required

● arrange the consideration and response of the commissioning body to the jurors' recommendations

From our pilots, we have estimated that a citizens' jury takes up at least 70 hours of the commissioning body's management time. However, we expect this to be reduced as we learn more about the process and share best practice.

Building a broad base

The citizens' jury is one among many possible ways of involving the public in decision making. It should not be seen as the best or only thing to do, but as part of a wider consultation process. Its credibility (and therefore its usefulness) will depend to a great extent on how it is regarded by local people and interest groups. Is it seen as a threat or an asset? As being imposed from outside the community, or generated within it? As part of a broad attempt to involve the public, or as an excuse for not consulting anyone but a handful of jurors?

It swiftly became apparent in our pilot series that a citizens' jury must not be allowed to take place in a vacuum. As a method of public consultation, it impacts not just on the commissioning body, but on other stakeholders in the area. During our first pilot in Cambridge and Huntingdon, for example, important organisations such as the local Unison branch and the

Community Health Council were not consulted at an early stage. As a consequence of this oversight, they were understandably suspicious that the jury was a ruse to bypass them and manipulate public opinion in the interests of the health authority. In later juries we found it invaluable to involve all the relevant local stakeholders in the planning stages.

We now recommend that an advisory group made up of all the stakeholders be convened by the commissioning body in order to help plan and develop the citizens' jury. This will be a useful source of advice and information, and a sounding board for ideas about the wording of the question, the shaping of the agenda and the selection of witnesses. It will help to allay fears of a "fix" and to build a consensual base for the jury.

Recruitment of jurors

For all five pilots, IPPR commissioned Opinion leader Research (OLR), an independent market research company, to recruit the members of the jury. It was felt that independence in the recruitment process was crucial in order to avoid either perceived or actual bias, as well as to ensure professional rigour. Questions may be raised about the merits of the different recruitment methods, but the separation of this function from the commissioning body has proved vital in building the credibility of the jury process.

Sixteen jurors are recruited to allow for some to drop out before the jury begins, without the total falling below 12. In our experience it is rare for recruited jurors to drop out and a jury of 16 has become the norm.

OLR has experimented with two methods of juror recruitment during our five pilots. Both methods draw upon a profile of the relevant area (e.g. the boundaries of a health or local authority) obtained from census or other demographic data, containing a breakdown of *social class, age, gender, ethnic background and housing tenure.* The two methods then differ quite significantly:

Method 1
A profile of a representative 16 person jury is weighted to reflect the five criteria as accurately as possible (for example, how many men/women of a certain class, age and ethnicity and housing tenure). Expert recruiters are then used to recruit the 16 jurors to match this profile. They use a combination of door-to- door visiting and approaching people in the street, until the profile quota is matched.

Method 2

Two thousand letters are sent out to residents in the area who are randomly selected from the electoral register, asking if they would be interested in taking part in citizens' jury. The letter gives only minimal information about the process (dates and duration) and no details about the subject to be addressed. Those who wish to take part are asked to complete a brief questionnaire to provide demographic data. Those who respond positively are matched to a profile of the area and grouped accordingly. Sixteen individuals are selected at random from these groups.[22]

There are advantages and disadvantages associated with each method. The first, which we used in CHHA, KCW/Riverside and Walsall, is open to accusations that it favours either mobile people who are out on the streets, or people who happen to be at home, or that recruiters may approach only certain kinds of people, or (worse still) only people whom they know. The second method avoids this problem, but is open to accusations of "self-selection", as it is only those who respond positively who form the recruitment pool.

It could be argued that both methods involve an element of self selection. A member of the public approached by a recruiter at home or in the street still has to agree or not agree to participate. On the other hand, they may respond differently according to whether they are contacted by letter or in person. At this stage, the second method appears to command more confidence and to provide a more accurate reflection of the targeted population. There is no suggestion that 16 individuals can ever be perfectly representative. However, our experience suggests that it is possible to recruit an appropriately wide range of people. In both Cambridge and Huntingdon and in Luton, local Community Health Council officers remarked on the organisers' success in obtaining a broad representation of their local community.

Payment

All jurors in our series were paid equally for their time (£200). We took the view that it would be unfair to have significant wage differentials reflected within the jury, and that equal commitment should be equally rewarded. The flat rate fee also goes some way to ensure that hidden costs (for example, child care for a non-working mother) are covered, and enables us to predict (and control) the cost of the jury process. All travel expenses are paid in addition. The £200 acts as a significant incentive, particularly for those on low incomes, who would not otherwise be willing or able to participate.

Some have claimed that this method acts as a disincentive for those on high incomes, who may lose money as a result of their participation, but this has not been borne out by experience. In each of the five pilots, we had no difficulty in attracting jurors from higher income groups. The jurors' own evaluations would appear to indicate that this method has been successful, but it should of course be tested against other strategies. What would be the effect, for example, of not paying jurors for their time? Would this bias the membership towards retired people or towards community-minded individuals?[23]

Screening

In our five pilot juries, we deliberately kept screening to a minimum, the terms of which were agreed with each commissioning body prior to the recruitment process. We agreed only to screen out individuals who were members of the board or council of the commissioning authority, senior employees of the authority who might have a conflict of interest, and elected Members of Parliament.

Some have questioned whether recruiters should screen out members of relevant interest groups, or people who have directly experienced a condition which the jury is being asked to discuss, such as mental illness or bereavement. However this poses further dilemmas: who should decide on exclusions and according to what criteria? And where is the line to be drawn? If individuals have experiences which bear directly upon the issue before the jury, these may be useful to its deliberations. We expect all participants to sometimes have past and present experiences of the issue, the important thing is that they address the issues in their capacity as citizens rather than users. So far we have found that jurors tend to approach their task from a community perspective, rather than thinking as selfish individuals and there have been no compelling reasons to screen more widely.

Some have argued that there should be no screening at all, or even that jurors should be recruited entirely at random. In Germany, *plannungzelle* members are selected at random, but the numbers involved are higher (25 instead of 16) and there is often more than one *plannungzelle* addressing the same issue. In our pilots we tried to balance the principles which have inspired the experiment with enough pragmatism to ensure that the model can be widely applied and does not fall into predictable traps. We decided that a jury recruited to achieve some degree of representativeness was less likely to incur criticism than a randomly selected jury that by chance excluded one or more significant groups.

Choosing the question

Choosing and refining the question for the jury and drawing up a manageable agenda are the most important and difficult parts of the whole process. From our experience, we have developed the following guidelines for authorities wishing to commission a citizens' jury:

The question should be a "live" issue which the authority needs to address
Jurors will take the process seriously if they are given a real question to answer. Attempts to mask the real issues, or ask "pretend" questions will lead to frustration, as well as being a waste of valuable time and resources.

The issue should be one which the authority is willing and able to act upon
It is no good asking jurors to decide upon an issue which an authority cannot or will not act upon. For example, there is little point in a locally-based authority asking a jury about an issue which would require action at a national level. This will lead to confusion and cynicism on the part of the jurors. Clear goal posts should be established at the start, defining the parameters within which the authority is willing and able to act after the jury has made its recommendations.

The authority should be prepared to hear an answer that it does not anticipate or like
If a question is worth putting to a citizens' jury, then the chances are it will involve a number of controversial issues or options. Juries are unpredictable, and there is no guarantee that they will opt for the authority's preferred answer. The decisions of a jury are not binding, but an authority should be prepared to respond fully to any recommendations with which they do not agree in an open and responsible manner.

The authority should be clear about what it wants from the jury process
This apparently simple ambition is quite hard to achieve in practice. Just wanting to know what members of the public "think" about a particular issue is not enough. Does the authority want a jury to come up with a clear proposal about a specific dilemma or problem, or does it really want help from the public in developing an overall strategy on a wider range of issues? The answer to this question will help to determine the way in which the question is framed.

Who does what?
Essentially, the commissioning body decides upon the line of questioning for the jury. This has led to some criticism that only those with the money

(for example, health authorities) will be able to set the agenda, and that their concerns (for example, maximising efficiency) may not be the concerns which members of the public wish to address. This problem can be addressed, although not entirely resolved, by convening a steering group to help develop the question and refine the agenda, as we suggested above (p.72).

Framing the question

Our pilots show that jurors are able to address complex issues. The real challenge is to frame the question in a way that is manageable, and to develop an agenda which enables them to reach a clear set of conclusions. It helps if the "headline" question for the jury is framed in a simple form. We had varying degrees of success with framing the question for our five pilots. In the first, Cambridge and Huntingdon, we were initially over-ambitious and asked the jury too many questions at a superficial level, rather than concentrating on one or two questions that could be considered in depth. One juror observed:

> *I think one of the problems is that when you think of a jury, you think of the jury having to decide if somebody is guilty or not guilty. In fact, what we are having to decide is about 500 different things ... it's made it a bit confusing. I imagine in the future it would be more simple and straightforward.*
>
> (CHHA juror)

With KCW/Riverside, we ran two juries on the same topic, which provided an opportunity to experiment with different ways of asking the main question. In the first KCW/Riverside jury, we asked: "What can be done to improve the quality of life for people with severe and enduring mental illness, carers and their neighbours?" The topic was broad and the question too vague. This may have reflected a lack of clarity on the part of the authority about their objectives for the jury. The question did not appear to focus on a real, "live" issue.

The question we put to the second KCW jury was: "What is good, bad and lacking in the services which are provided for people with severe and enduring mental illness?" On each day the jurors were asked to consider this question from a different perspective: users, carers and neighbours.

Although the two juries were considering the same issue, with the same witnesses, the question put to the second one was much clearer, and this made it easier for the jurors to move through the agenda. In all of our pilots, we found that it helped to keep the "headline" question down to one sentence if possible, and pinned to the wall, so that even if there were lots of secondary questions, the jurors (and the organisers) would always be reminded of the essential purpose of the four days' work.

Developing the agenda

A citizens' jury is essentially a decision making body, and the agenda should therefore be structured to enable the jurors to move purposefully through from the question/s to the point where they can make recommendations. The agenda is the framework which should give shape to the proceedings, whilst providing space for deliberation and sufficient flexibility to enable jurors to exert some control. It may be tempting to treat the jury as if it were merely the object of an information giving exercise. But this can result in the agenda being overloaded with witnesses, leaving little or no time for deliberation. During our pilots, we found that it was not satisfactory to leave deliberation until the final day, and that jurors were better able to make their final recommendations if they had time for deliberation on each of the four days, moving through a series of decisions. This also made it a more interactive and enjoyable experience.

For example in Walsall, jurors were presented with four options for improving palliative care. The agenda was planned to give jurors an opportunity to discuss and assess each model in turn, after hearing evidence. All four models were revisited on the final day, but by this time the jurors had identified and worked through most of the issues, were more confident in discussions with each other and were a lot more familiar with the subject before them. Consequently, a fairly robust and detailed list of recommendations could be drawn up and submitted to the health authority (p.20-22). However, one danger with this approach is that repetition becomes tedious. Jurors will soon complain if they are asked to answer the same question over and over again.

Developing case studies or options to present to the jurors ensured that the questions took on a concrete form. This was straightforward in Walsall, where the issue was essentially one of planning, but what of more general issues? In Cambridge and Huntingdon, jurors were asked for their views on how health authorities should set priorities – with a fairly general "headline" question. Jurors were then asked to consider specific case studies, to help identify their views on matters of principle (p.15-16).

From our pilots we conclude that jurors' capacity to deal with complex questions depends upon how the agenda is structured and on the skills of the moderators. In Cambridge and Huntingdon, jurors were asked on day three whether health care priorities should be set at a national or a local level. It was a complex and specific area of policy, and so we expected this to be the most difficult day. In fact, it was the most successful from the jurors' point of view. The day worked well because there was a clear cut question, with clear and distinct options for the jurors to consider. We had witnesses who openly disagreed with each other, empowering the jurors to make a real choice between their different perspectives.

> *I think it was the questions at the end that helped us to focus on what we're doing, and actually making a decision. I feel we're getting somewhere at last.*
>
> (CHHA juror)

> *We heard two viewpoints, but it was up to us to decide.*
>
> (CHHA juror)

In Luton, the options put to the jury (for funding the NHS) were not mutually exclusive and witnesses were less inclined to disagree with one another, often drawing attention to the ways in which different approaches to funding the NHS could be combined. Consequently, the jury's conclusions were less clear-cut. See Appendix 1, 2 and 3 for sample agendas.

The introductory evening

We found it useful to run an introductory evening for the jurors. This typically lasts for two hours on an evening shortly before the citizens' jury begins. The objectives are threefold: the organisers brief the jurors on the process; the commissioning body introduces itself and the question which it wants the jurors to address; jurors have the opportunity to meet each other, ask questions and if they wish, to change their mind about taking part. In practice, jurors have rarely dropped out following an introductory evening and then only because of work or personal commitments.

In our early pilots, we used the introductory evening to set out the issues for the week ahead, and jurors heard evidence from the Chief Executive of the health authority. However, many jurors said that this was too soon and that they would prefer to spend more time hearing about the process and getting to know each other. We followed this advice with the Luton jury, where it seemed to help build the jurors' confidence from day one.

Documentation for the jurors

Ample provision of information about the issue at stake is one of the distinguishing features of citizens' juries. Much, however, depends upon the amount, quality and accuracy of the information provided. In the early pilots we underestimated the amount of data jurors could accommodate, until their own evaluations revealed that they would prefer to have more rather than less written information whenever possible (see p.61-62).

During the five pilots we provided jurors with background briefing papers on the main issue before them, plus information about the commissioning authority. Each witness was encouraged to submit one page of text summarising their key points, which jurors could keep for reference. We tried to ensure that any written information was first submitted to the organisers, so that it could be checked for accuracy, purged of jargon and shortened if necessary. This also allowed the moderators to anticipate issues likely to come up during the discussions, and allowed jurors to prepare some preliminary questions before hearing from each witness.

Our initial fears that supplying written information would discriminate against the less literate jurors were not borne out by the jurors' own responses. However, it is clearly important to ensure that information is provided in a gradual and non-threatening way, and that it is presented only when it becomes relevant to the immediate discussion. The agenda should allow time for jurors to read, digest and discuss written information, as not all will have the opportunity to do so at home.

Evidence presented by witnesses, whether written or oral, is not expected to be impartial unless explicitly presented as such to the jury. Witness are otherwise invited to give their particular view point or perspective. During our pilots we sometimes found it necessary to provide jurors with factual briefing papers. We recommend that any papers claiming to be "neutral" should be carefully vetted by the independent organisers and that all such papers should circulated to other witnesses.

Witnesses

The fact that jurors receive oral evidence helps to make the sessions more interactive and can bring an issue to life, as jurors cross examine the witnesses. Jurors appreciate the opportunity to put their questions to experts and others with relevant experience. For many of the witnesses, it will be the first time that they have had to give account of their views or practice to the public, and this can be a disconcerting experience for them. Witnesses often remark on the seriousness with which jurors embark on their task and the robustness of their questions.

Choosing and briefing witnesses is time consuming and controversial, as it is open to abuse, error and misunderstanding. We set out below some of the lessons learned from the pilot series.

Selection

Witnesses should be selected to help the jurors to address the question before them, not simply to ensure that all the local stakeholders have their say. Ideally, at least half of the witnesses should be selected by an organisation independent of the commissioning authority. An advisory group of all the stakeholders should oversee the selection of the witnesses. This will reduce the risk of stakeholders feeling "left out" or clamouring for the right to address the jury directly; it will help to build a consensual base for the jury, as well as ownership of the results, and to ensure that all relevant viewpoints are given adequate space in the agenda. As a rule, the jurors are asked to make their own choice of one or two witnesses to be heard on the final day.

The jurors themselves are often fairly suspicious of the health authority's motives and of the witnesses who have been selected to speak to them.

> *Are we going to hear from any speakers who are not happy with the way things are... [T]here is a danger that what we're presented with is a beautiful picture of everything as being amazing, and we'll swallow it because we don't know any better.*
>
> (CHHA juror)

> *We've heard a lot from heads of departments. Is there anyone coming from further down the chain?*
>
> (CHHA juror)

> *I think that if you are going to present the four models which are all supposed to be of equal weight, then they should be presented as such. It was pretty obvious to pick up that there appeared to be a little bit of a hidden agenda.*
>
> (Walsall juror)

The CHHA jurors chose to call a local GP and a member of the local Community Health Council to give evidence on the final day. The Walsall jurors called an independent expert on palliative care. The first KCW/Riverside jury heard from witnesses on days one and two that black people were more likely to be diagnosed as suffering from mental illness. Although the organisers had taken care to ensure that users of mental health services gave evidence, none was black. At the jurors' own request, a black service user was called to give evidence on the final day.

It is reassuring to observe that jurors are keen detectors of the inveterate "fixing" impulses of public officials, but the selection of witnesses is clearly open to actual or perceived bias and abuse. The fact that jurors can call their own witnesses on the final day is a useful safeguard, but organisers should try to anticipate their suspicions and objections, in the interests of a balanced agenda. The witnesses should ideally not be selected by the commissioning body and as a minimum, we suggest that the steering group should perform this key function.

Quantity and quality of witness presentations
The jury has only four days. We found it tempting in the early juries to overcrowd the witness sessions with health care professionals, in an effort to explain what they "did", rather than using the time to explore the questions. With hindsight, it is clear that too many witnesses with too many different jobs and perspectives can confuse, rather than illuminate the issues.

One of the key lessons from the pilot series was the need to keep witnesses presentations short and to the point. In the first jury in Cambridge, we allowed witnesses to talk for up to 30 minutes, with only fifteen minutes for questions and answers. However, it quickly became evident that the longer the witnesses talked, the more inclined they were to slip into "conference mode" while the jurors slipped into a doze. Often the question and answer sessions proved the most useful and interactive, so in the following juries witnesses were asked to talk for fifteen minutes only, followed by 40 minutes questions and answers. This forced them to focus their evidence, and enabled the jurors to take a more active role in the proceedings.

We now recommend that there should be no more than four witness sessions per day, each leaving 40-45 minutes for questions from the jurors. It also helps if the jurors are given time to prepare some preliminary questions in pairs or small groups. The morning of the first day is usually devoted to a background briefing. The afternoon of the final day must be left for the jury to draw up its conclusions and recommendations.

At the time of writing we are experimenting with witness panels, with up to four witnesses giving evidence to the jury in one session and participating together in the following question and answer session.[24] This means that more voices can be heard by the jury but each witness can only give evidence for five to seven minutes. Our initial findings are positive, as the panel discussions enabled the jurors to hear opposing views together, allowing a thorough airing of all the issues. However, the usefulness of this method may depend upon the clarity of the issue, the degree to which witnesses differ in their views and requires thorough briefing of the witnesses.

Jurors' deliberations were often made more difficult by witnesses talking in abstract or jargon-laden terms. There was also a tendency for witnesses to try to be the "good guy" when confronted by a jury made up of members of the public, or to try to put forward only the "good news" about current service provision, so that important issues were glossed over. Soft-soaping and equivocation will not help the jurors any more than abstraction or exclusive, jargon-laden language. There is a strong case for holding a separate briefing session for witnesses, in order to help them understand the process and what is expected of them.

Almost invariably, jurors appeared to respect and appreciate evidence from service users and front-line workers, and to find this more animating than evidence from managers or academics. It is important to make sure that the jury does hear from "real people" as well as from "experts", but that neither type of evidence escapes close scrutiny. One of the strengths of the citizens' jury process is that jurors are given significant amounts of time to cross examine witnesses, and to contrast their evidence with that of other witnesses, as well as to check it against their own personal experiences.

Moderation

Each of the pilot citizens' juries was moderated by two skilled and independent professionals, with no specialist knowledge of the issue to be discussed. In essence, their role is to enable the jurors to move purposefully through from the question/s to the point where they can make recommendations. This is achieved by ensuring that the question is clear and that everyone has a say, facilitating discussions and debates through out the week so that jurors are able to reach substantive and confident conclusions on the final day.

The pilots demonstrated that moderating a citizens' jury is very different from moderating other types of group discussion. Unlike focus groups, for example, a citizens' jury brings together 16 people from diverse backgrounds.

The purpose is not to extract from people views which they did not know they possessed, treating individuals as objects of research, but to engage citizens in informed and interactive deliberation. In a citizens' jury, the moderator acts as enabler, encouraging the jurors to explore and debate the issues before them, by questioning witnesses and exchanging views.

The moderator must ensure that questions put to the jury are answered, without leading the process unduly, or overriding the jurors' legitimate concerns. This has proved to be a difficult balancing act to perform and problems can occur at both ends of the spectrum. In KCW/Riverside we tried two approaches, moderating the first in more open-ended and "hands off" manner than the second. In the first, the jurors did not seem to be empowered by the lack of moderation, but seemed to be struggling to achieve their objectives. A few jurors tended to dominate, and this caused resentment among others. In the second jury, the jury seemed to proceed in a more coherent and purposeful manner, and jurors were able to produce a clearer set of recommendations. However, some members of the second jury felt that the process had been too tightly controlled by the moderators. Clearly it is difficult to get the balance right, and judgements must be influenced by the kind of question which is being addressed, and by the personalities of the jurors themselves.

The majority of jurors in the pilot series were initially confused about the process ("What am I supposed to be doing here?") and overwhelmed by the evidence. It has been argued that a moderator who is also expert in the subject before the jury might help to ensure that jurors are clear about the facts, particularly if the issue is complicated or technical. The danger would be that an acknowledged "expert" might too readily lead the discussions, and their opinion carry too much weight, effectively disenfranchising the jurors. It may be that there are different models of moderation and/or facilitation which may be appropriate to different purposes. These issues need to be explored through further experimentation and evaluation.

Jurors' discussions

One of the distinctive features of a citizens' jury is that it is a deliberative process. Citizens reach conclusions based on evidence from expert witnesses, and informed and reflective discussions with their fellow jurors. It is important that enough time is built into the agenda for deliberation to take place throughout the jury. As a result of our experiences, we recommend several techniques for ensuring that all jurors have the opportunity to express and exchange their views.

In the first pilot jury, we assumed the moderators could best facilitate debates in the plenary sessions following evidence from witnesses. It soon became apparent that not all jurors were willing or able to express their views in front of sixteen people, despite the best attempts of skilled moderators. We now recommend that each day should provide an opportunity for jurors to break out into small groups, to allow them time to discuss the issues amongst themselves. Jurors are typically given a question to address relating to a witness session, such as "What are the strengths and weaknesses of this model?"

The small groups are not moderated, as this has proved to be unnecessary in practice. Each group nominates a spokesperson, who later reports its findings to the full plenary session. A moderated discussion then takes place, where the aim is to identify areas of agreement and difference and to explore the underlying reasons for the different viewpoints. The participants of each small group can be rotated to prevent the development of factions with polarised views. Jurors often report that they value the opportunity to exchange views with a wide variety of people. A combination of small and large group deliberation adds to the quality of that exchange.

It is sometimes useful to break the jury into pairs for brief discussions, such as preparing questions for witnesses. To ensure cross-fertilisation of views, it is useful to rearrange jurors' seating each day, so that they always have different neighbours.

Can jurors reach a consensus?

Jurors are asked to try to reach a consensus where possible, but this is never forced. It is perfectly valid for jurors to differ in their views, and disagreements are recorded. In Walsall, for example, the jury was supportive of the aims of the Sister Dora Hospice Appeal, but were unconvinced that this charitable organisation would have the capacity to raise the kind of money required to build a brand new hospice. Thirteen jurors therefore concluded that the prospect of a "hospice with a difference", provided by a partnership between the private sector and the voluntary sector, should be explored. Three jurors remained convinced that a dedicated hospital ward was the most attractive option, whilst the rest felt that a hospital was an inappropriate environment for people who are terminally ill.

It is worth noting here that the two KCW/Riverside juries, though asked slightly different questions and moderated in different styles, came to conclusions that were broadly similar. For example, the both juries called for improved communication and closer liaison between service providers and agencies, for more support for professionals in the field and for a 24-hour crisis centre. Both juries also called for more open and honest consultation with the community when the health authority considers the location of residential units, and recommended a review of drug policies.

The jurors' report

On the final day of the citizens' jury, jurors are asked to reach conclusions about the question/s before them and, if possible, to produce recommendations for the commissioning body. A report is then produced which briefly records the agenda, the witness sessions, the questions the jurors addressed on each day, any intermediate findings, and the jurors' final conclusions and recommendations. The report, once approved by the jurors themselves, is submitted to the commissioning body for their consideration, after which it becomes a public document.

Because of the time constraints, it is unrealistic to expect the jurors to write the report themselves. This method has been employed in America, as well as in a "consensus conference" organised by the Science Museum in the UK. It may be open to abuse, as one or two literate and/or opinionated jurors may effectively end up writing the report, which may not be a fair representation of the views expressed. We recommend that the report is written by an observer who is independent of the commissioning authority, who is present throughout the jury. We also recommend that the entire jury process is taped so that a written transcript may be produced if desired. The tapes provide a rich source of qualitative information, indicating not just what the jurors decided about a question, but how they reached that decision, and whether they changed their minds. Written data prepared for the jury, including background briefings and summaries of the witnesses' evidence, contribute to the record, and may be included in the body of the report or in appendices. Further information can be gathered from individual questionnaires given to jurors before and after the jury process. The report writer (in our pilots a member of IPPR) draws on these sources to draft the jurors' report.

The initial draft is circulated to all jurors, who are given the opportunity to amend or challenge any misrepresentations. This can be done via the post or by reconvening the jurors. In our experience, few jurors choose to challenge the wording of the report through the post. In three of our pilots we recalled the jurors to a special meeting to discuss the draft report. In

Walsall, this meeting was held one week after the event and fifteen out of sixteen jurors attended, without financial incentives. However, some jurors wished to alter the emphasis of their recommendations and this left us with a dilemma. What happens if jurors change their minds between the final verdict and the recall meeting? When does the jury end? What is the status of a post-jury meeting, and what if the decision of that meeting contradicts the recorded decision of the citizens' jury? On the other hand, in KCW/Riverside, only a handful of jurors turned up – perhaps because several weeks elapsed between the jury and the recall meeting. How then should the views of an interested minority be weighed against those of the unengaged majority? These are difficult questions which require further exploration. At this stage, we favour the postal system, as long as the report is based upon accurate records, drafted by a person independent of the commissioning body, and sent out to jurors no more than three weeks after the jury's final day.

When writing the report, it is important to be clear about who and what it is for. Is it an analysis of the jury process (perhaps an anthropological study) or is it a report of the jurors' deliberations and recommendations? We favour the latter, which calls for brevity and clarity rather than for interpretation or comment. Furthermore, our pilots indicate that it is important to submit the report to a board meeting of the commissioning body within six weeks of the jury. This helps to ensure that the momentum and enthusiasm generated by the jury is maintained, making a significant contribution to the perceived success of the citizens' jury.

Observers

In the interests of openness and in order to help build credibility for the jury process, we ensured that all of our pilots were open to observers. Typically, these included representatives of the local health authority, provider trusts, the Community Health Council and interested academics and journalists. It has been suggested that citizens' juries, like legal juries, should be held in public, so that justice, or fair decision-making, can be seen to be done. However, we chose to limit the numbers of observers, both because of the practical restrictions of space, and because we wished to avoid inhibiting the jurors' deliberations. We recommend that representatives of the key stakeholders should be invited to observe and the media encouraged to attend. It is worth scheduling observers' attendance, so that their numbers are evenly distributed through the four days. And we have developed guidelines for observers, to urge them not to talk to each other while the jury is sitting, nor to visibly agree or disagree with the opinions of witnesses or jurors, nor to expound their own views to jurors during breaks.

When questioned, the majority of jurors said that they did not think the jury should be open to the public in general, as it would inhibit their discussions and make them vulnerable to pressure or criticism. There is no proof that this is the case, however. If ways can be found to overcome the practical constraints, it would be worthwhile to test the hypothesis by holding a jury in public.

The media

A citizens' jury typically only involves up to sixteen people and, with space for observers limited, the media have a crucial role to play. The media can and do act as recorders and disseminators of the jury's deliberations, making the local community aware that a citizens' jury has taken place and with what effect. Two of our pilots were filmed. Although the cameras were initially inhibiting, a large majority of jurors claimed that after the first day they made no difference to their discussions.

It was possible to observe the effect of cameras in KCW, where we ran two juries on the same topic, only filming the second pilot. The second jury did not appear to suffer because of the presence of cameras, and indeed, it seemed to encourage the jurors to feel that they were being listened to and that they were engaged in an important process. This was also the case in Luton, where BBC *Newsnight* filmed for two days.

Some have criticised citizens' juries as being just another band wagon for the media to leap upon. However, this has proved to be a strength rather than a weakness, as the jury process offers a welcome "hook" upon which to hang some very important issues traditionally ignored by the media. This can provide the public with an opportunity to become more informed about the issue and makes it more difficult for commissioning bodies to ignore the voice of the public. The findings of every pilot citizens' jury were discussed at board level and the presence of the media evidently encouraged each board to provide a robust response. We hope that the media, especially local radio and press, can act as "watchdogs", helping to hold the commissioning body to their commitments by alerting the public and checking periodically whether they fulfil their promises. However, it is too early to tell how far this will actually happen.

As with all observers, the presence of reporters should be planned and scheduled in advance, so as to minimise interference. Careful thought must be given to how much access the media are allowed. For example, names and addresses of individual jurors ought not to be divulged without their consent and efforts should be made to ensure that jurors' views are fairly represented to the media. There are dangers in one of two vocal individuals becoming self-selected spokespeople for the jury. Equally, it can be problematic if some elements of the jurors' discussions are broadcast before they have reached their final conclusions, as this may misrepresent the views of some jurors or distort the deliberative process. All this points to the need for a well considered media strategy to be agreed between the organisers and the commissioning body, before the jury begins.

6. Lessons for democracy

In the first Chapter of this report, we set out the case for involving the public as active participants in decision-making. We briefly examined alternative models for public involvement and compared their characteristics. In Chapter Two we described the IPPR pilot citizens' juries and, in Chapters Three and Four, reported on their findings on health policy issues and on the jury process. In Chapter Five we set out our own observations about the process, with recommendations for making citizens' juries run smoothly, for building and sustaining their integrity as a model of public involvement, and for helping juries to produce outcomes which satisfy the jurors and the commissioning authority. Finally, in this Chapter, we consider the lessons for democracy. What have we learned about the capacity of citizens to participate in decision-making? What have we learned about the strengths and weaknesses of this particular method of involving the public? What are the lessons for public interest organisations who wish to involve the public in their decision-making? And where do we go from here: how should we proceed if we wish to continue to improve the quality and scope of public involvement?

The capacity of citizens

It is clear from our pilots that ordinary citizens are willing to get involved in decision-making processes. Efforts to recruit jurors through random mailings to names on the electoral register elicited a satisfactory response rate; once recruited, the jurors' drop-out rate was low (p.72). We have not tested how far payment affects enthusiasm, but there is some evidence to suggest that, when people are asked to give up a considerable amount of time, they may be less likely to agree if there is no financial incentive or compensation.[25]

The pilots indicate that most jurors are reasonably well able to deal with quite complex issues and to scrutinise and assimilate arguments and data. Their capacity to do so depends to a great extend upon the question and agenda being prepared in an appropriate and manageable form. Gaining some knowledge of how to do this has been an important outcome of the pilot series. Right from the start, however, we were deeply impressed – as were most other observers – with the level of competence with which jurors tackled their task. Almost all of them appeared in time to participate with confidence, although inevitably this came more easily to some individuals than to others.

Some of the topics addressed by the juries were more demanding than others. The jury model appears to lend itself more effectively to choosing between clearly-defined options or developing guidelines for decision-makers, rather than to producing detailed plans or considering abstract ideas. In one of the pilot juries (Luton) we received comments after the event from one witness and one observer, both expressing concern that some jurors seemed to have failed to grasp key points in the argument. This jury considered alternative ways of funding the NHS – probably the most technical and demanding topic put to any of the IPPR pilots (p. 24). With hindsight, we might have reduced the options considered by the jury from four to three or even two, or organised the witness sessions differently, with each option having a clear advocate for and against. The Luton jurors' final conclusions were nonetheless an honest and substantial representation of their views.

Perfect understanding by all jurors of all aspects of the topic before them can probably never be proved and should not be expected. Juries are intended, after all, to be one component in a decision-making process, not the final arbiter. In spite of deficiencies of process in the pilot phase and the human failings of some jurors, the prognosis is in our view more heartening than disheartening. In each jury, as the days progressed, we observed jurors becoming more sceptical about the quality of evidence and witnesses brought to them, more alert to the dangers of being hoodwinked or misled, more keenly aware of their own abilities and limitations as decision-makers, and better able to distinguish between decisions they could take as jurors and those better left to experts. Much depends on the skills of the moderators in helping to encourage the less confident jurors and preventing the more confident ones from dominating the proceedings.

It appeared to us that most jurors behaved as though they were acting on behalf of their community rather than simply in their own best interests. The experience of being selected to represent the local population and taking part in a "jury" with fellow citizens seemed to produce a peer-group pressure to be "good neighbours" and to consider the needs of others. Very few jurors were prepared to assert their personal interests over those of the community as a whole and we were struck by how seldom jurors used personalised anecdotes as a means of expressing a view or interpreting evidence. We have not tested how long this effect lasts and whether it carries over into decisions made by individual jurors after the jury.

Similarly, it appeared that citizens' juries could encourage other forms of active citizenship by building up individuals' confidence and exposing them to ideas about what they might be able to do. Several jurors expressed interest in getting involved in other community related activities after their jury experience. For example, one of the Walsall jurors who at first insisted she could not serve because she didn't know enough about the subject and "wasn't clever", ended by inquiring how she could stay involved in decisions about health. One of the KCW/Riverside jurors was inspired to seek training as a therapist, so that she could work with people who suffered from mental illness.

Anyone who has observed or participated in one of these juries could not easily sustain the view that these members of "the public" are apathetic, ignorant or selfish, or that they are untrustworthy or unsuitable to play more than a walk-on part in a decision-making process. Perhaps they could have been all of these things but, given the chance to be otherwise, they rose to the challenge. In short, there is far more enthusiasm, ability and "community spirit" among ordinary citizens than most decision-makers routinely assume. What has been lacking is the opportunity for that capacity to be demonstrated (to the citizens themselves as much as to the decision-makers) and put to good use.

The role of citizens' juries in decision-making

We have already suggested how, in particular respects, citizens' juries compare with other methods of public involvement. Here we look briefly at the potential and the limitations of the citizens' jury model in relation to different kinds of decision-making.

The great strength of citizens' juries is the opportunity they provide for informed deliberation. This would suggest that they may be better at tackling complex questions and difficult choices than other models. Undoubtedly, however, the juries' capacity for in-depth qualitative decision-making relies heavily on the skills of the moderators and on the clarity and precision with which the agenda is prepared and witnesses selected and briefed. A well-organised and skilfully moderated jury can be expected to address complex and difficult issues successfully, but a poorly organised and moderated jury will probably fail.

Because it involves so few individuals at any one time, a citizens' jury can only be seen to represent the community *symbolically*. We have discussed the difficulties of finding recruitment methods which are not vulnerable to criticism of one kind or another. No recruitment method is entirely watertight. The organisers should be open about their recruitment techniques and take care not to make claims about the representativeness of the jury which cannot be substantiated. The fact that a citizens' jury cannot be precisely representative underlines the importance of seeing its decisions as advisory rather than binding, and as one component in a broader public involvement exercise (see below, p.94).

In some communities it may be impracticable to use the jury model – for example, where there are several minority languages. We have not yet attempted a jury with simultaneous translation in several languages, and before we embark on anything so costly and elaborate, we would prefer to explore other methods which may work better in a multi-lingual context. However, a citizens jury due to take place in Wales, on the subject of genetics, will be conducted in English and Welsh.[26]

Citizens' juries are relatively time-consuming and costly. They are not suitable for minor or extremely straightforward decisions, or for exercises whose purpose is purely to inform or impress the public. One commentator has suggested that there are two main types of jury: deliberative and decision-making.[27] Whether a jury is one or the other depends on the question put to it and on the intentions of the commissioning body. The first considers a policy or a problem and produces observations and/or proposals ("How can we improve services for the mentally ill?") The second is asked to make a choice between specific options ("Is route A, B or C the best one for the new road?") Both are valid, but it is useful to be clear at the outset which type is intended. In either case, however, the jurors may themselves decide to alter the approach – for example (as in Walsall) by refusing to choose one particular option, and setting out instead a list of aims and priorities.

The momentum of a citizens' jury tends towards consensus. Although jurors do not have to reach a unanimous verdict, and there are ample opportunities to discuss differences and record disagreements, the model we have developed, with emphasis on extensive deliberation, appears to encourage mutual understanding, compromise and consensus-building. We observed, for example, that in the course of four days, many of the jurors became more sympathetic about the dilemmas confronting decision-makers, especially the difficulties of distributing finite public funds. They were keen for their proposals to be taken seriously by the commissioning authority and took care not to make over-ambitious demands.

Consensus building may not be all that is required of a public involvement exercise. Sometimes it is equally useful to air fears and hostilities and to draw out points of disagreement. For any decision-making process it is important to identify different view-points and factions. This calls for other methods and may help to prepare for a citizens' jury.

A jury is more likely to be successful if it is held before views become entrenched. Once they are polarised and feelings are running high on a controversial policy issue, it may be futile to ask a citizens' jury to consider it. This may happen where politics and religious faith are closely intertwined (for example abortion), where factionalism entirely dominates decision-making (for example constitutional change in Northern Ireland), or where protest has become a strong identity for significant numbers (for example the route for a controversial bypass). We did not encounter such conditions in the pilot series, but we assume that it would be impossible to proceed unless representatives of the different viewpoints could be persuaded to join a steering group and to agree the question/s and agenda for the jury.

Ultimately, citizens' juries may be considered no less useful for what they can demonstrate to the wider public than for what they actually decide about the question/s before them. They show what ordinary people are capable of and how decisions can be made in an open, informed, reflective and co-operative manner. They suggest what might be achieved by this and other models. As we have noted, the media play a crucial role in getting such messages across. If they distort the picture, or if they do not or cannot report on what happened, the value of any jury will be undermined.

A citizens' jury can bring significant benefits to the commissioning authority. It can help to resolve a dilemma and to reach a better decision. It may do this by bringing new ideas and experience to the decision-making process. But it may also encourage the authority to think more carefully about what it wants to achieve and why, to scrutinise its own assumptions and to be more open about its own deliberations. A jury may, as we have noted, help to avert conflict and build consensus. It can boost the authority's confidence in the capacity of local citizens to participate constructively in decisions. And it can help to build the trust of local people in the integrity and competence of the authority.

On the other hand, a jury may "backfire" and compound the authority's problems if the model is used inappropriately, or if it is poorly prepared, or thought to be rigged in any way, or subject to bias, distortion or manipulation. It is therefore absolutely essential to establish clear and transparent rules of procedure and to safeguard the integrity of the process.

Lessons for decision-makers

Any organisation wanting to involve the public should be clear about its intentions and its capabilities. For example:

- Does it have a particular problem or face a particular dilemma and does it genuinely want help in resolving this? Or does it just want to know how the public will respond to a pre-determined decision, or to persuade the public to its point of view?

- What outcome/s does it desire – for example approval or a quiet(er) life, particular advice, rating of a prior decision or a choice between options?

- If the public are to be involved, what does that mean? Does the organisation want to involve users of a particular service or the wider community? To whom will the question be addressed?

- Who has an interest in the consequences of any decision? How strong are local feelings? Whose voice is loudest?

- How much freedom does the organisation have to act on the views of the public? What are the consequences of an unpredicted outcome?

- How much time has it got and what can it afford to spend on public involvement?

The answers to these questions should help the organisation to decide upon the method it will use to involve the public. The key point is to *match purpose to method*. For example, if the aim is to find out how the public will respond to a pre-determined decision, an opinion poll or survey may be the best choice, while a citizens' jury or deliberative poll may be a better way of helping to resolve a problem or dilemma. If the organisation knows that it must opt for a particular decision, however difficult or painful that might be, then it may have to try to persuade the public that it has done the right thing – in which case a public awareness or public relations campaign may be the only possible course of action. If one vociferous campaign with minority backing is dominating local debate, a jury may help to broaden the discussion, but it will be important to ensure that representatives of the campaign are involved in a steering group. If the organisation wants help with a decision about improving or changing a particular service, it may be best to invite the views of users of that service, but if the question is about distributing resources among a range of services, then a citizens' jury may be appropriate. In any event, shortage of time or money may limit an organisation's choice of methods. It may be advisable to choose a less expensive way of involving the public than to try to run a jury "on the cheap" and, by cutting too many corners, put the credibility of the process at risk.

Where any major decision is concerned and public involvement contemplated, the organisation should consider involving all of the following categories:

- experts

- stakeholder or interest groups

- service users where appropriate

- citizens

Each of these categories has an important contribution to make and each probably requires a different method of involvement. For example, stakeholder groups may respond to invitations to a meeting, or may be successfully consulted by means of a qualitative survey. Experts and stakeholder groups can help to prepare ground for an exercise involving the general public, by clarifying issues and questions, providing background information and preparing options.[28] Alternatively, the views of citizens or stakeholder groups may be solicited in order to inform a decision which is ultimately taken by experts. It is up to the organisation to decide which arrangement is best in which circumstances. But the four categories cannot substitute for one another. In our view an organisation which sought to involve ordinary citizens (through a jury or any other means) but ignored local interest groups, would be jeopardising the quality of its decision-making, no less than if it took the public to be adequately represented by user groups or if it consulted only the experts. In any event, if a citizens' jury is to be held, it should be part of a broader exercise involving dialogue with stakeholders as well as with experts, and should not be allowed to stand as the sole expression of public opinion.

For the future

Looking forward from the IPPR pilot series, we have identified the following objectives for the future:

● *To refine the citizens' jury process,* encouraging a range of organisations to commission them and to run them, so that all can learn from a wide variety of ideas and experience. So far we have worked with health authorities and local authorities. Utility companies, government agencies, industry regulators and voluntary organisations have also expressed interest in commissioning juries and may do so within the next 12-18 months.

● *To develop and share appropriate skills,* for example, in recruitment and moderation, in agenda setting and the recruitment and briefing of witnesses, in writing jury reports and disseminating their findings. The demand for juries is in danger of outstripping the supply of skills and experience needed to run them effectively.

● *To promote further innovation.* Lessons learned from citizens' juries as well as from other models, such as deliberative polls, consensus conferences, citizens' panels and electronic forums, should be applied to further innovation, continuing to develop new ways of involving the public. In particular, we are interested in models which share the essential characteristics of a jury (time, information, scrutiny, deliberation and independence), but which are able to extend these to wider numbers, or which require fewer human and financial resources. At the time of writing a two-day jury has just been completed with apparent success and a series of "television juries" is being planned. These and other innovations, eg interactive citizens' forums and other forms of "teledemocracy", should be encouraged.

● *To monitor citizens' juries beyond the pilot series, as well as further innovations in public involvement.* Monitoring will point to problems and possibilities and help develop ideas for refining citizens' juries and other models.

● *To develop a collaborative project* or network of groups who are actively interested in citizens' juries and other new forms of public involvement, to promote the exchange of ideas, experience and skills.

● To identify and spread best practice. Any form of public involvement is only as useful and authoritative as its reputation. It must be seen by all the parties involved and by the wider public as being:

fair: not rigged or distorted by poor procedures

incorruptible: not led to pre-determined outcomes by the commissioning body, or vulnerable to lobbying by outside interests.

authentic: clear about what it claims to be and seen to fulfil those claims.

effective: able to reach meaningful conclusions which make an impact on the decision-making process.

Identifying and spreading best practice will help to build and sustain the integrity of these processes, and public confidence in them.

In conclusion

Levels of public – and political – interest in new ways of involving the public are remarkably high, and appear to be rising. We anticipate many more citizens' juries, commissioned and conducted by an increasingly wide range of organisations. We also anticipate continuing innovation and experimentation, not only in forms of dialogue and discussion, but also in the application of new technologies and the adaptation of various models for television programming. We welcome all these developments, which for us underline the importance of collaborative working and of careful monitoring and evaluation.

As innovations of this kind proceed, questions are likely to intensify about their integrity, their effectiveness and their role in democracy. How can they be trusted? Whom do they represent? How should they relate to elected representatives and public bodies? Are they a threat to our political institutions or a useful resource? Can they deepen the democratic process or will they be used to railroad unpopular or poor decisions? Much depends on how the different models are developed, what is claimed on their behalf, how they are applied and how they are perceived. For juries to succeed, they must be credible and reliable. If poor practice were to undermine confidence in them, they would soon lose their appeal and their value. At some point, it may be necessary to go beyond sharing knowledge and skills and spreading "best practice", to develop an agreed set of guidelines by which citizens' juries (and perhaps other models) are conducted.

SELECTED BIBLIOGRAPHY

Barber B (1984) *Strong Democracy: Participatory democracy for a new age*, University of California Press.

Barnes M *et al* (1966) "Users, officials and citizens in health and social care", *Local Government Policy Making*, Vol 22 (4), Addison Wesley Longman, Harlow.

Bynoe I (1996) *Beyond the Citizens' Charter*, IPPR, London.

Commission for Local Democracy (1995) *Taking charge: The rebirth of local democracy*, MJ Books, London.

Cooper L *et al* (1995) *Voices Off: Tackling the Democratic Deficit in Health*, IPPR, London.

Coote A (ed) (1992) *The Welfare of Citizens*, IPPR/Rivers Oram, London.

Dienel P (1992) *Die Planungszelle*, Westdeutscher Verlag, Opladen.

Fishkin J (1991) *Democracy and Deliberation: Participatory politics for a new age,* Yale University Press, New Haven.

Fishkin J (1995) *The Voice of the People: Public Opinion and Democracy*, Yale University Press, New Haven.

Held D (1993) *Prospects for Democracy*, Polity, Oxford.

Keane J (1988) *Democracy and Civil Society*, Verso, London.

McNulty D (1995) *Referenda and Citizens' Ballots, Commission for Local Democracy*, University of Greenwich, London.

O'Leary S (1996) *European Citizenship – the options for reform*, IPPR, London.

Parry G *et al* (1992) *Political Participation and Democracy in Britain*, Cambridge University Press, Cambridge.

Prior D *et al* (1995) *Citizenship: Rights, community and participation*, Pitman, London.

Renn O *et al* (1993) "Public participation in decision making: A three-step procedure", *Policy Sciences,* 26, Netherlands.

Stewart J (1995) *Innovations in Democratic Practice*, Institute of Local Government Studies, Birmingham.

Stewart J (1996) *Further Innovations in Democratic Practice*, Institute of Local Government Studies, Birmingham.

Stewart J (1997) *More Innovations in Democratic Practice*, Institute of Local Government Studies, Birmingham.

Stewart J, Kendall E and Coote A (1994) *Citizens' Juries*, IPPR, London

Stoker G (1997) "Local political participation", *New Perspectives on Local Governance*, Joseph Rowntree Foundation, York.

Young S (1966) "Stepping Stones to Empowerment? Participation in the context of Local Agenda 21" *Local Government Policy Making*, Vol 22 (4), Addison Wesley Longman, Harlow.

References

1 Held D (1993) *Prospects for Democracy*, Polity, Oxford pp18-21
2 See Bynoe I (1996) *Beyond the Citizens' Charter*, IPPR, London
3 Prior D *et al* (1995) *Citizenship: Rights, community and participation*, Pitman, London.
4 Stewart J (1995) *Innovations in Democratic Practice*, Institute of Local Government Studies, Birmingham.
5 O'Leary S (1996) *European Citizenship – the options for reform,* IPPR, London.
6 Renn O *et al* (1993) "Public participation in decision making: A three-step procedure", *Policy Sciences* 26, 189-214, Netherlands: 205.
7 Keane J (1988) *Democracy and Civil Society*, Verso, London p4
8   Stewart J (1996) *Further Innovations in Democratic Practice*, Institute of Local Government Studies, Birmingham p2.
9 Stewart J (1995) *op cit*; see also Stewart J (1996) *op cit.*
10 *Runaway World: People and Politics in the Late Modern World*, was the title of a conference in January 1997 to coincide with the publication of Anthony Giddens: *Critical Assessments* by Routledge. The Conference was organised by the Institute of Contemporary Arts in collaboration with Routledge, IPPR, Polity Press and King's College, Cambridge; see also Beck U, (1973) *Risk Society.*
11 Stewart J, Kendall E and Coote A (1994) *Citizens' Juries*, IPPR, London p 4-5.
12 Renn O *et al* (1993),*op cit.*
13 McNulty D (1995) *Referenda and Citizens' Ballots, Commission for Local Democracy,* University of Greenwich, London.
14 Thomson W (1992) "Realising Rights through Local Service Contracts" in Coote A (ed) *The Welfare of Citizens*, IPPR/ Rivers Oram, London p129-52.
15 Stewart J (1995) *op cit.*
16 For a fuller discussion of both models see Stewart J *et al* (1994) *Citizens' Juries*, IPPR, London 9-51.
17 A copy of this video is available from Kensington, Chelsea and Westminster Health Authority.
18 Cambridge and Huntingdon, KCW/Riverside 2, Walsall and Luton; the first KCW/Riverside questionnaires were lost.
19 These reports are available from each health authority or the IPPR on request.
20 This section of our report builds on observations set out in *Citizens' Juries: Towards Best Practice*, a document produced in October 1996 by IPPR and Opinion Leader Research for organisations interested in commissioning or organising citizens' juries.
21 Stewart J *et al* (1994) *op cit*

22 This method was first used for recruiting a citizens' jury by Richard Cuper at the University of Hertfordshire, who recruited an organised a jury on waste management for Hertfordshire County Council.

23 In a citizens' jury in Sunderland, held in January 1997 as part of the King's Fund pilot series, the organisers deliberately did not tell the jurors that they would be paid. They found it difficult to to recruit young people.

24 IPPR and OLR have recently experimented with this method in Camden, where a citizens jury looked at the redevelopment of a local site.

25 See note about the pilot jury in Sunderland, *op cit.*

26 Details from the Welsh Institute for Health and Social Care, University of Glamorgan.

27 Bill New of the King's Fund made this distinction after observing the Cambridge and Huntingdon jury.

28 This is similar to an approach described in Renn O *et al* (1993) "Public participation in decision making: A three-step procedure", *Policy Sciences* 26,189-214, Netherlands.

Appendix 1: Walsall Citizens' Jury

Question: What are the priorities for improving palliative care services for people who are terminally ill in Walsall?

Introductory Evening: Wednesday 14th August 1996

7.00pm **Introduction and welcome.**
The moderators introduce themselves to the jurors, explain what a citizens' jury is, and the question which we wish them to address.

7.20pm **Michael Evans, Chief Executive, WHA.**
Michael Evans explains the role of the health authority.

7. 30pm **Questions and answers**

7.45pm **Dr. Christina Faull, Consultant in Palliative Care**
Dr. Faull explains simply what "palliative care" is, and the different ways of caring for people with terminal illnesses.

7.55pm **Questions and answers**
Jurors given the opportunity to ask Ms Faull questions about palliative care, or the moderators about the process which they are participating in.

8.10pm **Cheryl Towers, Counsellor** explains that she and two colleagues (Derek Coombe and Pauline Oflerne) will be available for telephone calls if necessary.

8.15pm **Exercise**
Jurors participate in a brief "getting to know you" exercise.

8.30pm **Questionnaires**
Jurors asked to fill in a brief pre-jury questionnaire.

8.50pm **Contract signing**

9.00pm **Close**

Walsall Day One: Saturday 17th August 1996

10.00am   Welcome and recap.
Jurors are welcomed, and reminded of the key issue which they are to address throughout the week, and the key issue of the day: What *criteria* should we use to help us choose between different models of palliative care?

10.15am   Ms Anne Bailey, Walsall Breast Cancer Support Group.
Ms Bailey explains her experience of providing palliative care to the terminally ill, and suggests possible criteria which could be used when selecting a model of care.

10.30am   Questions and answers

11.00am   Dr. John Linnane, Consultant in Public Health Medicine, WHA.
Dr. John Linnane describes the needs for palliative care in Walsall and the present services, discussing the medical view of the criteria that should be considered in developing future services.

11.15am   Questions and answers

11.45am   Exercise
Jurors asked to suggest what factors (criteria) a health authority should use when deciding how much, and what kind of palliative care to purchase.

12.30pm   Lunch

1.15pm   Barbara Collins, Chief Officer, Community Health Council
Ms Collins explains from a users and carers' perspective the issues which are important when deciding upon the type of palliative care.

1.30pm   Questions and answers

2.00pm   Michael Evans, Chief Executive, Walsall Health Authority.
Mr. Evans explains the financial arrangements for the Authority, and how decisions on priorities for investment are reached.

2.15pm   Questions and answers

2.45pm   Coffee break

3.00pm   Exercise
Jurors asked to develop criteria for judging the different proposals through a combination of small and plenary group work.

4.30pm   Close

Walsall Day Two: Sunday 18th August 1996

10.00am	**Model 1: Palliative care at home** The moderators briefly talk through model 1.
10.15am	**Pam Swift, Macmillan Nurse** The nurse explains in her own view what is good and bad about this (and other) models of palliative care.
10.30am	**Questions and answers**
11.00am	**Break**
11.15am	**Mrs X, Carer** This witness talks about their experience of palliative care, and what they think is good and bad.
11.30am	**Questions and answers**
12.00am	**Model 2: Inpatient hospice** Moderators briefly talk through this model
12.15am	**Lunch**
1.15pm	**Mike Marshall, Sister Dora Hospice Appeal** Mr. Marshall explains the advantages and disadvantages of this and other models according to his experience.
1.30pm	**Questions and answers**
2.00pm	**Dr. Debbie Pearson, Consultant in Palliative Care and Medical Director of Compton Hospice.** Dr Pearson explains the advantages and disadvantages of this and other models according to her experience.
2.15pm	**Questions and answers**
2.45pm	Jurors split into three groups, and asked to assess the two different models which they have heard about according to their own criteria.
3.30pm	Jurors regroup, and one member from each of the three reports back on their findings to the others.
4.00pm	Jurors asked what witnesses (if any) they would like to call for the morning of day four.
4.30pm	**Close**

Walsall Day Three: Thursday 22nd August 1996

10.00am	**Model 3: The Hospital** The moderators briefly talk the jurors through this model
10.15am	**Dr. Rod Brookes, Consultant Geriatrician, Walsall Hospitals Trust and Dr. P. Carpenter.** The doctors explain what the advantages and disadvantages of this and other models are in his experience.
10.30am	**Questions and answers**
11.00am	**Break**
11.15am	**Dr. Ian Poole, GP**
11.30am	**Questions and answers**
12.00am	**District Nurse** Explains her role, and answer jurors questions about palliative care and the models.
12.15pm	**Questions and answers**
1.00pm	**Lunch**
1.30pm	**Model 4: Nursing Homes Specialising in Palliative Care** Moderators briefly talk through this model.
1.40pm	**Ms. Susan Cooper, Director of Nursing, APTA Health Care** Ms Cooper explains the advantages and disadvantages of this and other models according to her experience/perspective
1.55pm	**Questions and answers**
2.20pm	**Ms Joyce Bennett, Hospital Social Work Team** Ms Bennett explains the advantages and disadvantages of this and other models according to her experience/perspective
2.35pm	**Questions and answers**
3.00pm	**Break**
3.15pm	Jurors break into three groups to assess the two models according to their criteria.
4.00pm	Jurors report back on their findings to each other.
4.30pm	**Close**

Walsall Day Four: Friday 23rd August 1996

10. 00am   Jurors hear from own witnesses, **Mike Marshall** of the Sister Dora Hospice Appeal and **Bruce George MP**.

11.00am   Jurors debate and discuss the different options in small and large groups. In the plenary session, moderators attempt to identify areas of agreement and difference, and prepare draft recommendations which can be presented to the expert in the afternoon.

12.30am   **Working lunch**
Jurors present their initial thoughts and ideas to **Peter Tebbit**, an independent consultant for the National Council for Hospice and Specialist Palliative care Services. (At the jurors request). He will assess how feasible their proposals are, and advise them on any practical issues.

1.30pm   Jurors finalise recommendations, through a moderated session

2.45pm   **Break**

3.00pm   Jurors present their main findings to **Michael Evans**, CE, who makes an initial response and thanks the jurors for their help.

3.30pm   Jurors fill in the various questionnaires and evaluation forms.

4.15pm   Collect money and goodbyes.

4.30pm   **Close**

Appendix 2: Luton Citizens' Jury

Question: How should citizens pay for health services in the future?

Introductory Evening, November 19th 1996

7. 00pm	**Introductions and welcome** The moderators introduce themselves to the jurors, explain what a citizens' jury is, and the question which we wish them to address
7. 30pm	**Questions and answers**
7. 45pm	**Developing ground rules** Moderators encourage jurors to develop ground rules for ensuring that everybody has a fair say during the coming week.
8. 15pm	Jurors sign contracts and fill in questionnaires
8. 45pm	**Close**

Luton Day One: 23rd November 1996

10.00am	**Recap on ground rules for the citizens' jury**
10.30am	**Jurors exercise:** What has changed for the better in the NHS over the years? What has changed for the worse?
11.15am	**Coffee**
11.30am	**Witness 1. Dr. Marion Barnes, HSMC** Background to the NHS – when it was created, why and how it is currently funded and (briefly) organised.
11.45	**Questions and Answers**
12.30pm	**Lunch**
1.30pm	**Witness 2. Dr. Alan Maryon Davies** Future issues for the health service – an overview of the likely challenges e.g. rise in elderly, new technologies, increased demand.
1.45pm	**Questions and Answers**
2.30pm	**Introduction to the four funding models** Moderators briefly read through, and ensure that everybody understands what they will be doing in the forthcoming days.
2.45pm	**Coffee**
3.00pm	**Small group work.** Jurors encouraged to develop criteria for assessing the different funding mechanisms by. What is important to them as citizens?
3.45pm	**Plenary session.** Jurors report back to each other on their discussions, and the moderators try and draw out some common agreement for general principles/criteria which the juror think are important when considering how to pay for health services.
4.30pm	**Close**

Luton Day Two: 25th November 1996

10.00am   Welcome and recap.

10.15am: Model 1: Private Insurance
Moderators allow time for jurors to read through the model and prepare questions.

10.30am   Witness: David Bryant, Head of Public Relations, BUPA
Argues for an increased role for private insurance. This may involve reducing the NHS to a core service, whilst "extras" are provided through private insurance.

10.45am   Questions and answers

11.30am   Coffee

11.45am   Small group work
Jurors split up and discuss the strengths and weaknesses of this model, compared to the other two.

12.15   Plenary session
Jurors report back to each other on their discussions.

12.45pm   Lunch

1.30pm   Model 2: General Taxation
Moderators allow time for jurors to read through the model and prepare questions.

1.45pm   Witness: John Appleby, University of East Anglia and Norwich
Argues that taxes are the most efficient and fair way of paying for the NHS, and that if we wish to increase (or maintain) NHS funding, then it should be from general taxation.

2.00pm   Questions and answers

2.45pm   Coffee

3.00pm   Small group work
Jurors split up and discuss the strengths and weaknesses of this model, compared to the other two.

3.45pm   Jurors report back to each other in the plenary session, and share their assessments of the models.

4.30pm   Close

Luton Day Three: 26th November 1996

09. 45am   Model 3: User Fees
Moderators allow time for jurors to read through the model and prepare questions.

10.00am   Witness: Dr. Goldsmith, suggests that there might be a role for user fees for some types of health services

10. 20am   Questions and answers

11. 00am   Coffee

11.15am   Small group work
Jurors discuss the advantages and disadvantages of this model.

12. 00am   Plenary session
Jurors report back to each other on their discussions.

12. 30pm   Lunch

1. 30pm   Model 4: Hypothecated Taxes/Insurance
Moderators allow time for jurors to read through the model and prepare questions.

1.45pm   Witness: Jon Ford, BMA argues that governments may need to "ring fence" taxation for the NHS in order to guarantee that it will be spent on the NHS, and therefore enable them to raise additional revenue, if required.

2.00pm   Questions and answers

2.45pm   Small group work
Jurors should split up and discuss the strengths and weaknesses in each model. Which do they prefer and why?

3.15pm   Coffee

3.30pm   Plenary session.
Jurors report back to each other. Moderators identify areas of agreement and difference.

4.00pm   Jurors are asked to suggest which witnesses they would like to hear from on the morning of day four.

4.30pm   Close

Luton Day Four: 27th Novembeer 1996

10.00am	**Welcome and recap.**
10.15am	**Jurors call own witnesses** **Bob Angel**, Chief Executive of Luton and Dunstable Hospital (a local trust hospital)
12.30	**Lunch**
1.30pm	Moderators draw together the jurors recommendations, focusing on which model they prefer, and why, using a combination of small and large group work.
3.00pm	**Questionnaires etc.**
4.00pm	**Thanks and money etc.**
4.15pm	**Close**

Appendix 3: Camden Citizens' Jury

Questions: How could the Swiss Cottage site be improved? How can these ambitions be achieved?

INTRODUCTORY EVENING: Wednesday 5th March

7.00pm	**Introduction and welcome.** Explain what a citizens' jury is. The question that will be answered will be explained, background papers given out. Quickly through agenda.
7.30pm	**Welcome from Amanda Kelly, Deputy Chief Executive of Camden Council.**
7.45pm	**Questions and answers**
8.00pm	Walk through the site to see it at night.
8.30pm	Jurors sign contracts and fill in questionnaires.
9.00pm	**Close**

Camden Day One: Saturday 8th March

10.00 am **Recap from introductory evening.**
Jurors warm up exercise: What are the best things about the site, what are the worst?

10.30 am **Witness: Christopher Wade, local historian**: Background to the site: history of buildings and the community's use of the site.

10.45am **Questions and answers**

11.30am **Coffee**

11.45am **Witness: John Mothersole, Director of Leisure and Community Services**: Background to the project. The limitations and conditions of the development (parameters which the council will impose and the jury must work within). Listing. An introduction to the trade-offs necessary. An explanation of the need to cost and finance all the proposals.

12.00am **Questions and answers**

12.45pm **Lunch**

1.30pm **Witness: Clive Burley, planner:** The overall planning situation in Camden, other changes which may affect decisions on the site.

1.45 pm **Tour of site with Clive Burley**

3.00pm **Questions and answers followed by: Small group work**
The jury decides upon a list of overall objectives for the site and for the whole local area.

3.45 pm **Coffee**

4.00 pm **Plenary session: Feedback on objectives.**
Moderators draw together the objectives to develop a list of criteria by which evidence can be judged.

4.30 pm **Close**

Camden Day Two: Monday 10th March

How would you improve the site taking account of what's there?
What would you add, what would you take away?

10.00am	**Welcome and recap.**
10.15am	Jurors prepare questions for panel of witnesses
10.30am	What is good and bad about the open space. How can it be improved? **Panel of witnesses:** **1 young user of the sports space: Miowa Griffith** **1 rep of market: John Rolf** **1 resident: Elaine Chambers** **Open space consultant: Adrian Wikely**
11.00am	**Coffee**
11.15am	**Questions and answers**
12.15pm	**Small group work:** What's good/bad about the open space. How could it be improved?
1.00pm	**Lunch**
1.45pm	**Plenary:** Feedback.
2.15pm	Jurors prepare questions for the next witnesses.
2.30pm	What do the current site occupants want from the site? What are the changes they want and how do they intend to finance their proposals? **Panel : Theatre: Richard Wakely** **Sports Centre: Grant Wright** **Library: Eileen Murphy**
2.50pm	**Questions and answers**
3.45pm	**Coffee**
4.00pm	**Small groups:** What is good and bad about what the site occupants have suggested? Jurors suggest own witnesses.
4.30 pm	**Close**

Camden Day Three: Tuesday 11th March

10.00am Recap. Jurors prepare questions.

10.15am What do the current site occupants want from the site? How should their proposed changes be financed?
**Panel: Community Centre: June Turner,
            Winchester Centre: Graham Good**

10.30am Questions and answers

11.15am Coffee

11.30am **Small group work:**
What are the advantages and disadvantages of the proposals to changes to the buildings?

12.00pm Plenary

12.30pm Lunch

1.15pm **Small group work**
The jurors' own suggestions for the site. What do you want, how can it be funded?

2.00pm **Plenary**
Moderators draw together the open space and buildings work to get a list of priorities so far. The jury decides on a series of rough proposals and questions to put to the next panel concerned with the viability of ideas in three areas:
1) **Finance:** a) any new money which could come in from housing.
               b) how the trade offs could work together.
2) **Planning**
3) **Existing people on site**

3.00pm Coffee

3.15pm **Panel of witnesses:**
**Independent consultant: Graham Tulley, Drivers Jonas
Planner: Clive Burley (open space advocate)
Finance: John Mothersole
Community advocate: Richard Graham**
Will not give presentations but will answer questions concerned with the three areas.

4.30pm **Close**

Camden Day Four: Wednesday 12th March

10.00am	**Recap**
	Large group work commenting on the responses of the last panel.
10.30am	Jury prepares questions for their own witnesses.
10.45am	Jury's own witnesses chosen at the end of day 2. Possibly a panel drawn up already so that the jury can put its proposals to them.
12.30pm	**Lunch**
1.15pm	**Small/large group work**
	Moderators draw conclusions together. The jury sets out priorities for what it wants compared to the sacrifices needed for costing.
3.00pm	The jury presents their conclusions to **Amanda Kelly**
3.30pm	**Questionnaires, money and thanks.**
4.15pm:	**Close**